BLETCHLEY PARK

BRAIN TRAINING
PUZZLES

BLETCHLEYPARK

This edition was published in 2015 by the Bletchley Park Trust
The Mansion, Bletchley Park, Milton Keynes, MK3 6EB

ISBN: 978-1-78404-413-8
AD004280NT

Cover design by Rose
Printed in the UK

CONTENTS

INTRODUCTION

During World War Two, Bletchley Park was a workplace to thousands of people whose job it was to read the encrypted messages of its enemies. Towards the end of 1941, a crossword puzzle competition was organised by the Daily Telegraph. The challenge was to complete the puzzle in under 12 minutes. A Mr Gavin, Chairman of the Eccentrics Club offered to donate £100 to the Minesweepers Fund, if it could be done under controlled conditions. As a number of the competitors were subsequently invited to take part in intelligence work at Bletchley Park, puzzles and Codebreaking have been linked in the public mind ever since the exploits of Bletchley Park's Codebreakers became public knowledge.

Codebreaking is very much a puzzle solving process and the codes and ciphers used are similar to the most common types of puzzles such as crosswords, word searches and sudoku. In many cases, the Codebreakers of Bletchley Park were looking for patterns in the problem before them, much like puzzle solvers today. Both often also base their solutions on clues. For example, a simple code might represent words by something else such as strings of numbers. In this case, the clue may lie in the frequency of certain strings of numbers occurring in the encrypted message. Straight or quick crossword clues are simple definitions of the answers so the clue lies in the definition provided. A more difficult cipher might replace each letter in a message with another letter of the alphabet twice, a so-called double-encryption. This is a bit like cryptic crosswords in which the clues are puzzles in themselves.

Encrypted WW2 enemy messages were usually transmitted in groups of letters, typically 4 or 5 in length. So when the letters were decrypted, they would still be in these letter groups but some letters might be missing. The Codebreakers would then have to piece the actual words of the message together. This is a bit like a 'fill-in-the-blank' clue in crosswords or word search puzzles.

So you see puzzle solving is synonymous with the profound intellectual feat and remarkable brains of those whose work at Bletchley Park is said to have helped shorten WW2 by up to two years. Following in this long-held tradition, the Bletchley Park Trust has today produced this series of Puzzle Books so that you can follow in the footsteps of the Codebreakers and perhaps establish whether you have the puzzle solving skills needed to have worked at wartime Bletchley Park...

1 Domino Placement

A standard set of twenty-eight dominoes has been laid out as shown. Can you draw in the edges of them all? The check-box is provided as an aid, so that you can see which dominoes have been located.

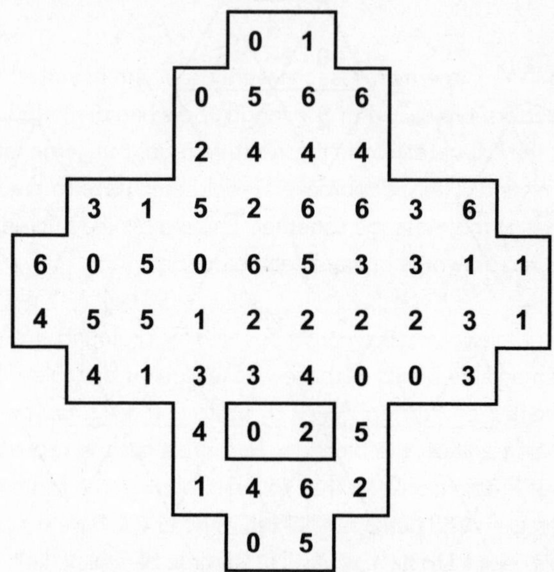

0-0	0-1	0-2	0-3	0-4	0-5	0-6
		✓				

1-1	1-2	1-3	1-4	1-5	1-6	2-2

2-3	2-4	2-5	2-6	3-3	3-4	3-5

3-6	4-4	4-5	4-6	5-5	5-6	6-6

Hexagony

2

Can you place the hexagons into the grid, so that where any hexagon touches another along a straight line, the contents of both triangles is the same? No rotation of any hexagon is allowed!

3 Simple as A, B, C?

Each of the small squares in the grid below contains either A, B or C. Every row, column and each of the two long diagonals has exactly two of each letter. The information in the clues refers only to the squares in that row or column. To help you solve this problem, we have provided as many clues as we think you will need! Can you tell the letter in each square?

Across

1 The Bs are between the Cs
2 The As are further right than the Bs.
3 Each C is next to and left of an A.
4 Each C is next to and left of a B.
5 The As are between the Bs.
6 The As are between the Bs.

Down

1 The Bs are between the Cs.
2 The Cs are between the As.
3 The Bs are between the Cs.
4 The Cs are not in adjacent squares.
5 The Cs are between the As.
6 The Cs are higher than the As

	1	2	3	4	5	6
1						
2						
3						
4						
5						
6						

Total Concentration

4

The blank squares below should be filled with whole numbers between 1 and 40 inclusive, any of which may occur more than once, or not at all.

The numbers in every horizontal row add up to the totals on the right, as do the two long diagonal lines; whilst those in every vertical column add up to the totals along the bottom.

Can you discover the missing numbers?

								143
	26		21	35	6	13	17	127
18		32	16	14	20	32		199
8	34	27	37			29	21	198
	35	33	15	28	24	10	31	192
38	17	3		8		19	22	153
22		19	9	28	33		30	163
24	1	40	7		13	36		146
9	33	25		18	12		11	172
139	199	184	150	158	151	182	187	169

5

Shape Up

Every row and column in this grid originally contained one circle, one diamond, one square, one triangle and two blank squares, although not necessarily in that order.

Every symbol with a black arrow refers to the first of the four symbols encountered when travelling in the direction of the arrow. Every symbol with a white arrow refers to the second of the four symbols encountered in the direction of the arrow.

Can you complete the original grid?

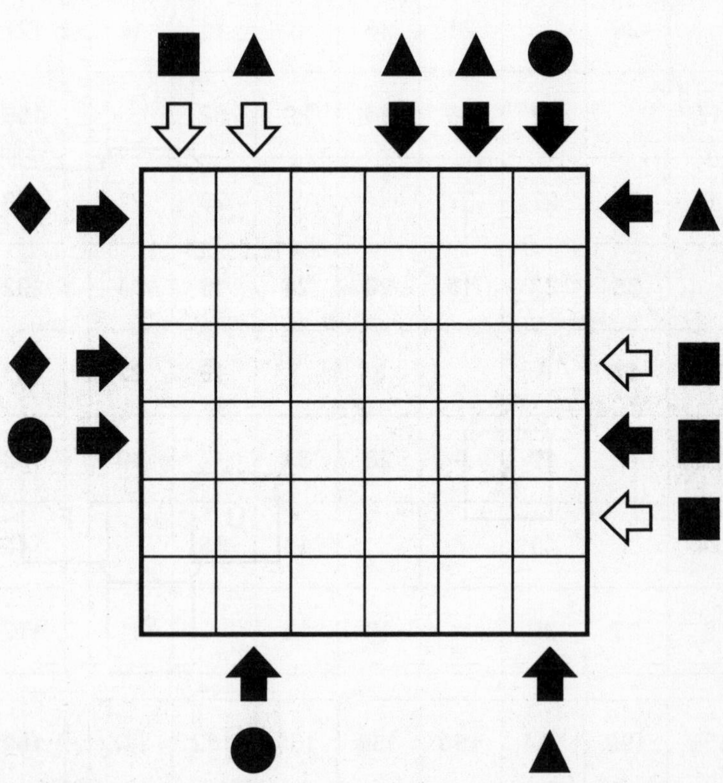

Mind Over Matter

Given that the letters are valued 1-26 according to their places in the alphabet, can you crack the mystery code to reveal the missing letter?

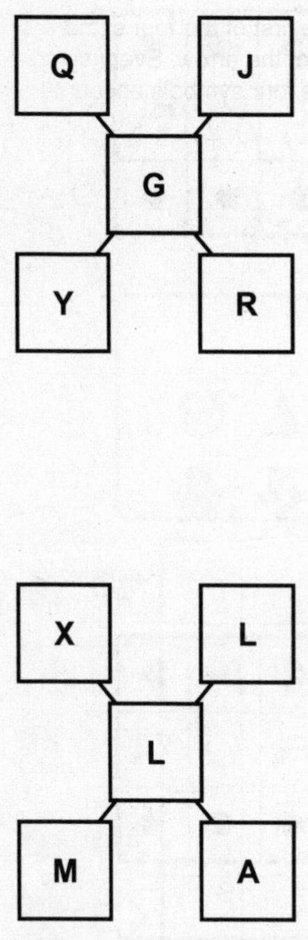

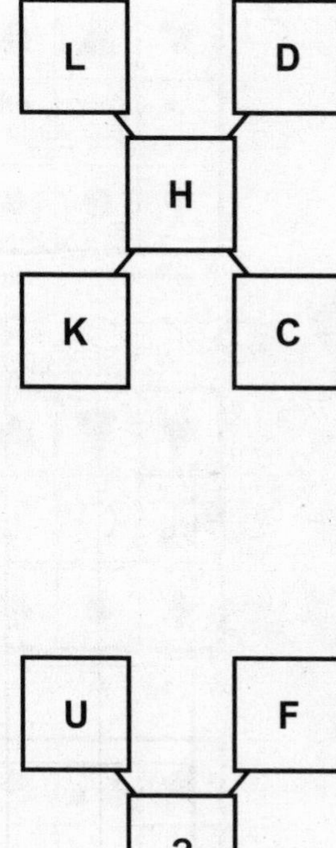

7

Whatever Next?

Which of the four lettered alternatives (A, B, C or D) fits most logically into the empty square?

1

2

3

4

?

A

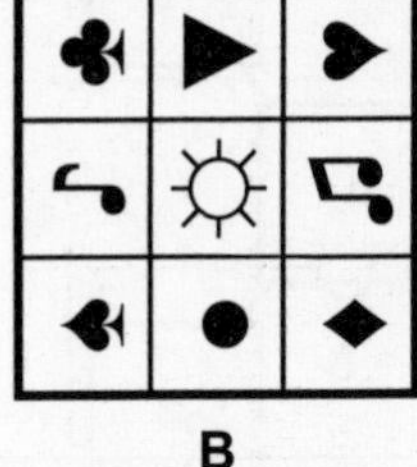

B

C

D

The Bottom Line

8

Can you fill each square in the bottom line with the correct digit?

Every square in the solution contains only one digit from each of the lettered lines above, although two or more squares in the solution may contain the same digit.

At the end of every row is a score, which shows:

a the number of digits placed in the correct finishing position on the bottom line, as indicated by a tick; and

b the number of digits which appear on the bottom line, but in a different position, as indicated by a cross.

					SCORE
A	7	2	5	1	✓ ✗
B	6	9	9	4	✓ ✗
C	6	7	1	1	✓
D	8	8	9	1	✗
E	3	3	3	5	✗
					✓ ✓ ✓ ✓

9 Combiku

Each horizontal row and vertical column should contain different shapes and different numbers.

Every square will contain one number and one shape and no combination may be repeated anywhere else in the puzzle; so, for instance, if a square contains a 3 and a star, then no other square containing a 3 will also contain a star and no other square with a star will contain a 3.

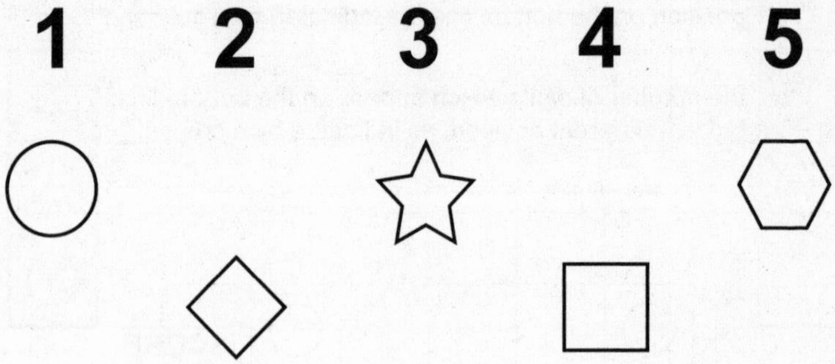

1 2 3 4 5

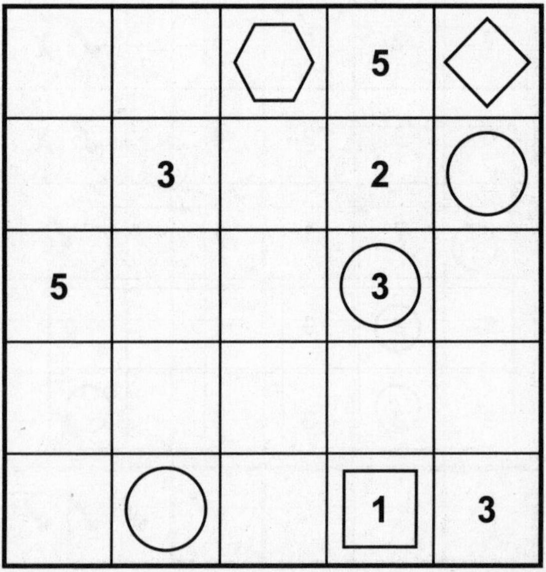

			5	
	3		2	
5			3	
			1	3

Ls in Place

10

Twelve L-shapes like the ones here need to be inserted in the grid and each L has one hole in it.

There are three pieces of each of the four kinds shown here and any piece may be turned or flipped over before being put in the grid. No pieces of the same kind touch, even at a corner.

The pieces fit together so well that you cannot see any spaces between them; only the holes show. Can you tell where the Ls are?

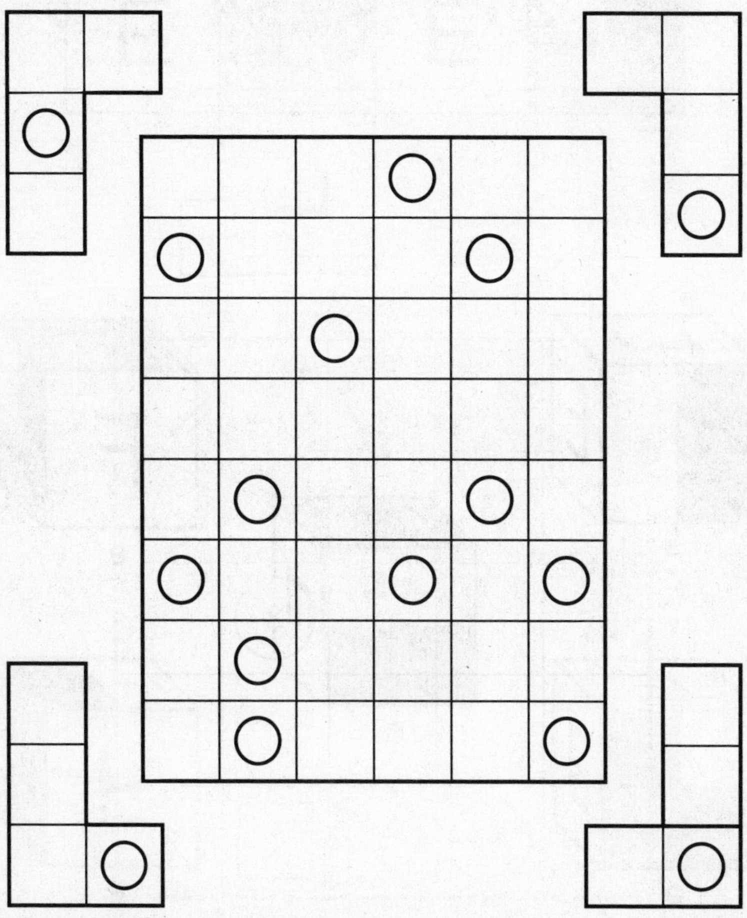

11

Box Clever

When the box below is folded to form a cube, just one of the five options (A, B, C, D or E) can be produced. Which?

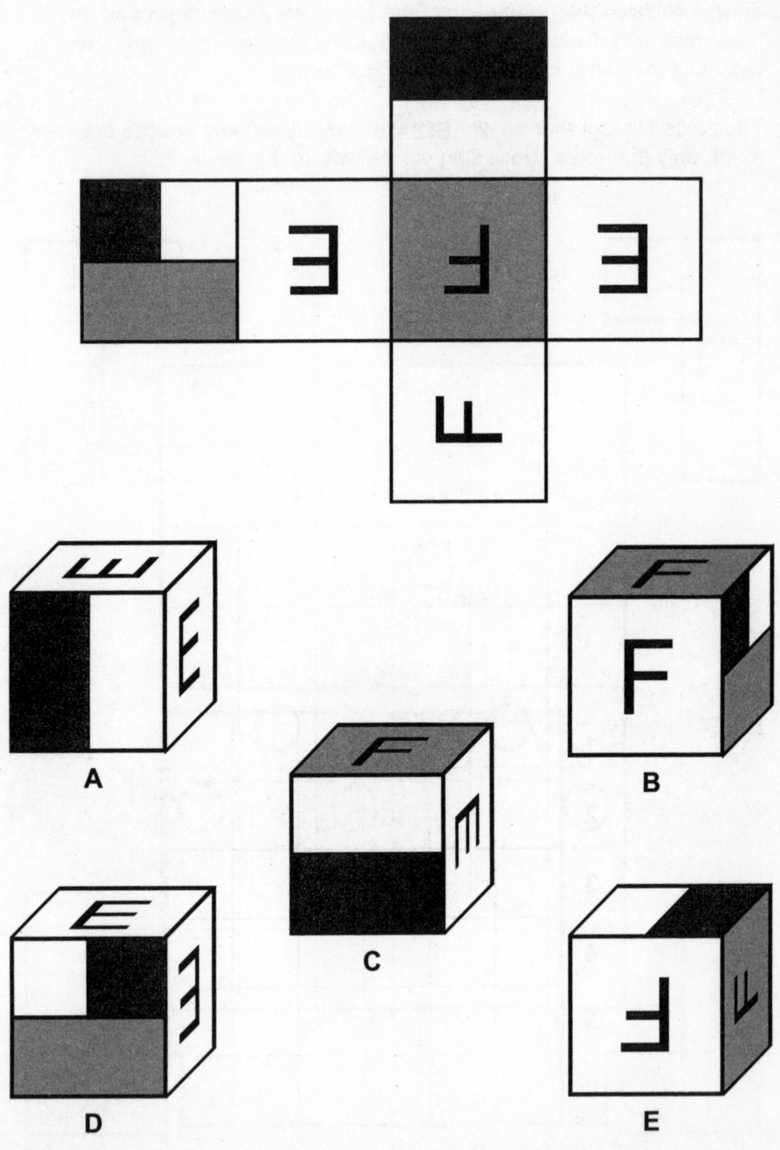

Latin Square

The grid should be filled with numbers from 1 to 6, so that each number appears just once in every row and column. The clues refer to the digit totals in the squares, eg A 1 2 3 = 6 means that the numbers in squares A1, A2 and A3 add up to 6.

1 D345 = 7

2 E12 = 5

3 F34 = 8

4 AB1 = 6

5 AB2 = 10

6 BC3 = 7

7 AB4 = 3

8 EF5 = 5

9 CDE6 = 12

10 A56 = 4

11 B56 = 11

12 CD2 = 4

	A	B	C	D	E	F
1						
2						
3						
4						
5						
6						

13

Number Link

Working from one square to another, horizontally or vertically (never diagonally), draw single continuous paths to pair up each set of two matching numbers. No line may cross another and none may travel through any square containing a number.

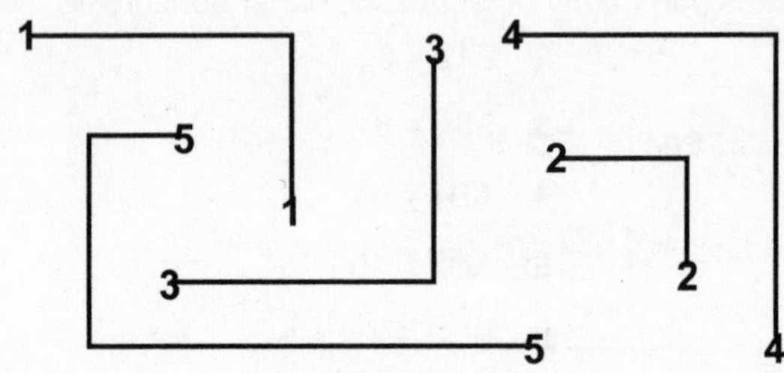

								2
					8			
			7	3	4			
								2
								9
9	6	8			4		1	1
7					3			6
5								5

Battleships

Can you place the vessels into the diagram? Some parts of vessels or sea squares have already been filled in. A number to the right or below a row or column refers to the number of occupied squares in that row or column.

Any vessel may be positioned horizontally or vertically, but no part of a vessel touches part of any other vessel, either horizontally, vertically or diagonally.

Empty Area of Sea: ≋

Aircraft Carrier:

Battleships:

Cruisers:

Submarines:

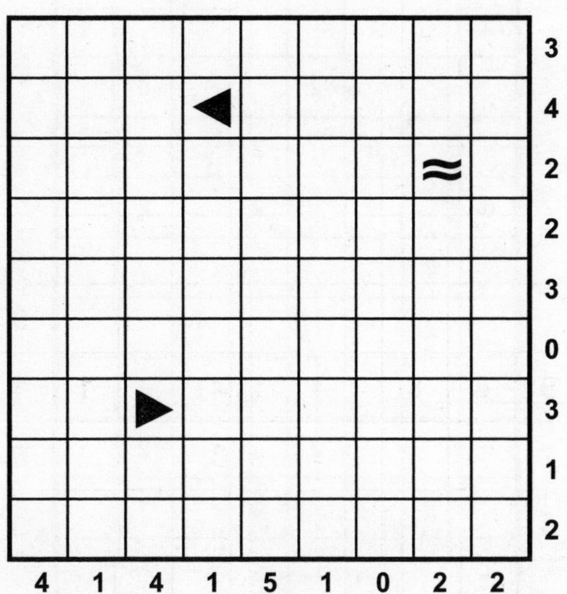

15 Coin Collecting

In this puzzle, an amateur coin collector has been out with his metal detector, searching for booty. He didn't have time to dig up all the coins he found, so has made a grid map, showing their locations, in the hope that if he loses the map, at least no-one else will understand it... However, he didn't count on YOU coming across the strange grid (as seen here). Will you be able to discover the correct number of coins and their precise locations?

Those squares containing numbers are empty, but where a number appears in a square, it indicates how many coins are located in the squares (up to a maximum of eight) surrounding the numbered one, touching it at any corner or side. There is only one coin in any individual square.

Place a circle into every square containing a coin.

0				3			
		3		4		3	
2		1					1
			2			0	
		0		2			
0				2		2	
	0						
	2				3		
			1	1	1	3	
			2			2	
	3			4		1	
2							

Slitherlink

16

Draw a single continuous loop, by connecting the dots. No line may cross the path of another.

The figure inside each set of any four surrounding dots indicates the total number of surrounding lines.

2	1			2			0	1	
1	2			1	0				
2		2						1	1
		2				0	1		1
1		1	0			1			1
		3	1			2			
							3	1	1
3				2		1			
2			2	1		0	0	2	
1	1		2	1				2	
	3				0		2	1	
3	2		2		1		3	1	2

17

Spot Numbers

The numbers at the top and on the left side show the quantity of single-digit numbers (1-9) used in that row and column. The numbers at the bottom and on the right show the sum of the digits. A number may appear more than once in a row or column, but no numbers are in squares that touch, even at a corner. Two numbers are already in place.

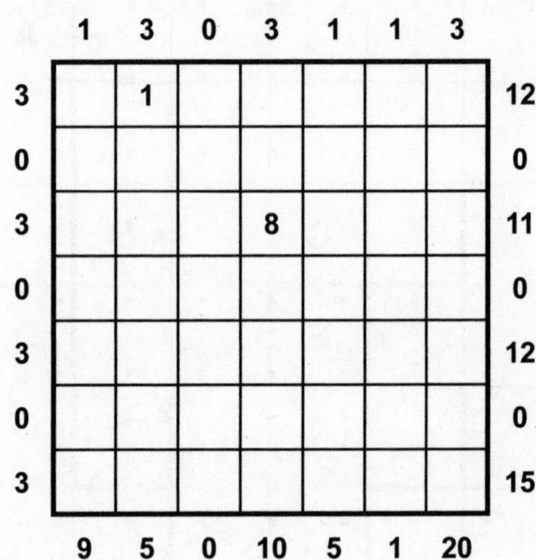

	1	3	0	3	1	1	3	
3		1						12
0								0
3				8				11
0								0
3								12
0								0
3								15
	9	5	0	10	5	1	20	

Logi-6

18

Every row and column of this grid should contain one each of the letters A, B, C, D, E and F. In addition, each of the six shapes (marked by thicker lines) should also contain one each of the letters A, B, C, D, E and F. Can you complete the grid?

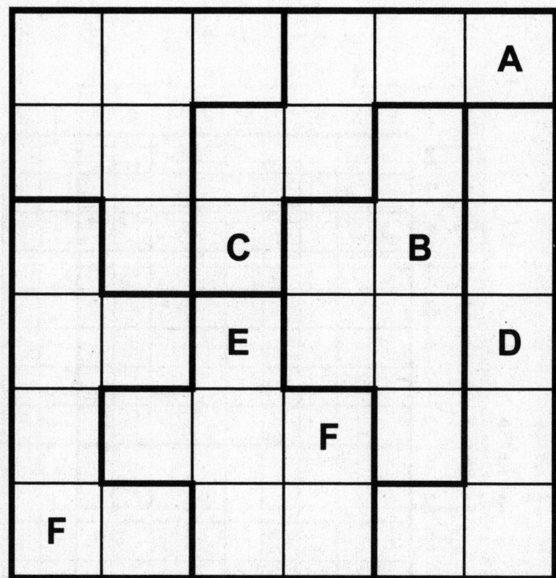

19

Piecework

Place all twelve of the pieces into the grid. Any may be rotated or flipped over, but none may touch another, not even diagonally. The numbers outside the grid refer to the number of consecutive black squares; and each block is separated from the others by at least one white square. For instance, '3 2' could refer to a row with none, one or more white squares, then three black squares, then at least one white square, then two more black squares, followed by any number of white squares.

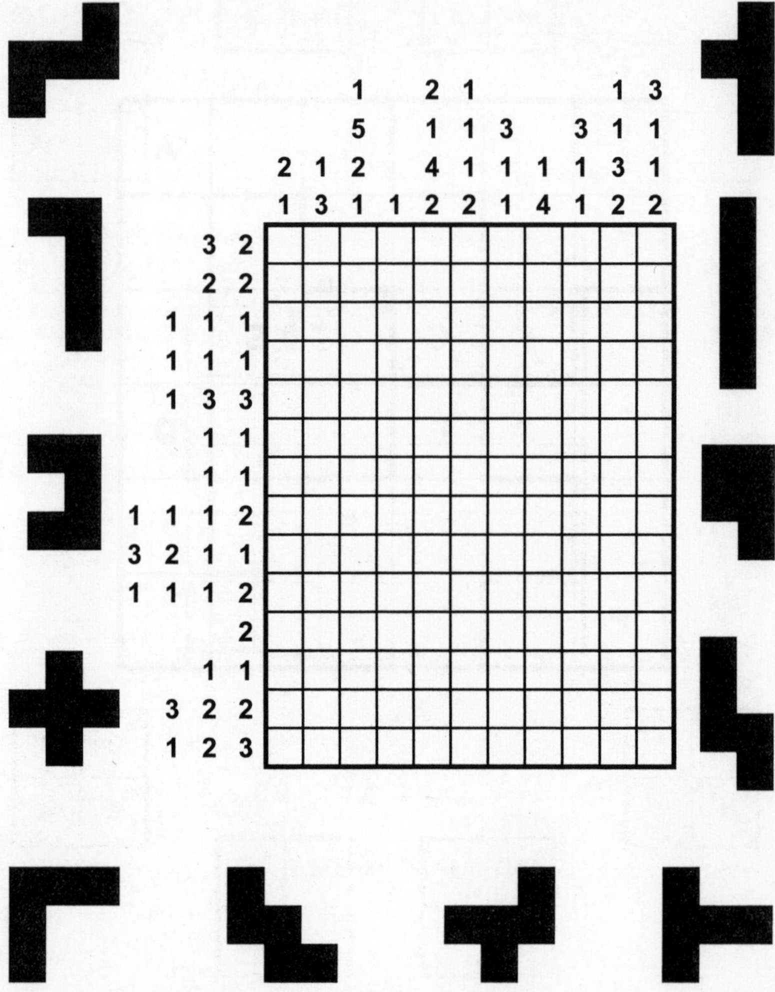

Tile Twister

Place the eight tiles into the puzzle grid so that all adjacent numbers on each tile match up. Tiles may be rotated through 360 degrees, but none may be flipped over.

1	4
1	4

1	1
4	3

1	2
2	3

1	4
2	1

				4	2
				3	3

4	3
1	1

3	1
3	4

2	4
1	1

4	1
1	3

21

Domino Placement

A standard set of twenty-eight dominoes has been laid out as shown. Can you draw in the edges of them all? The check-box is provided as an aid, so that you can see which dominoes have been located.

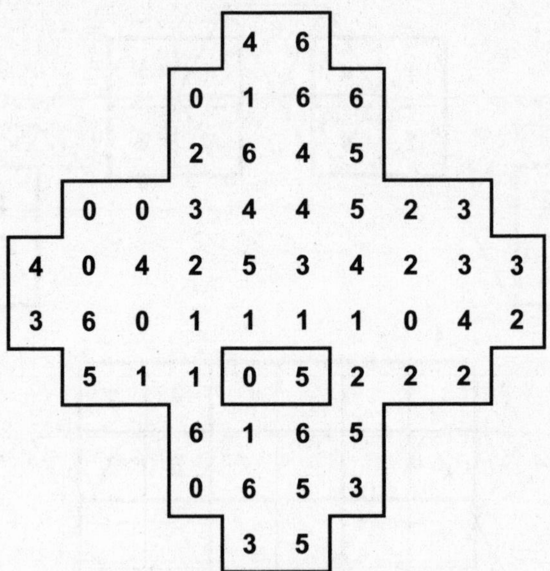

0-0	0-1	0-2	0-3	0-4	0-5	0-6
					✓	

1-1	1-2	1-3	1-4	1-5	1-6	2-2

2-3	2-4	2-5	2-6	3-3	3-4	3-5

3-6	4-4	4-5	4-6	5-5	5-6	6-6

Hexagony

Can you place the hexagons into the grid, so that where any hexagon touches another along a straight line, the contents of both triangles is the same? No rotation of any hexagon is allowed!

23 Simple as A, B, C?

Each of the small squares in the grid below contains either A, B or C. Every row, column and each of the two long diagonals has exactly two of each letter. The information in the clues refers only to the squares in that row or column. To help you solve this problem, we have provided as many clues as we think you will need! Can you tell the letter in each square?

Across

1 The As are between the Bs.
3 The Bs are between the Cs.
4 The As are between the Bs.
5 The Bs are further left than the As.
6 The Cs are further right than the Bs.

Down

1 The As are higher than the Cs..
3 The As are between the Cs.
4 The As are higher than the Cs.
6 Each B is next to and below a C.

	1	2	3	4	5	6
1						
2						
3						
4						
5						
6						

Total Concentration

24

The blank squares below should be filled with whole numbers between 1 and 40 inclusive, any of which may occur more than once, or not at all.

The numbers in every horizontal row add up to the totals on the right, as do the two long diagonal lines; whilst those in every vertical column add up to the totals along the bottom.

Can you discover the missing numbers?

								184
	21	5	15		23	16	25	180
27	15	14	20	39	1			176
16		19	18	8		22	29	170
25	6		37	10	28	12		174
19	24	3	23		20		17	138
26	20	30		31		7	37	201
	9	34	26	18	19	21	32	199
27	20		4	11	21		21	164
220	137	181	176	165	165	143	215	183

25 Shape Up

Every row and column in this grid originally contained one circle, one diamond, one square, one triangle and two blank squares, although not necessarily in that order.

Every symbol with a black arrow refers to the first of the four symbols encountered when travelling in the direction of the arrow. Every symbol with a white arrow refers to the second of the four symbols encountered in the direction of the arrow.

Can you complete the original grid?

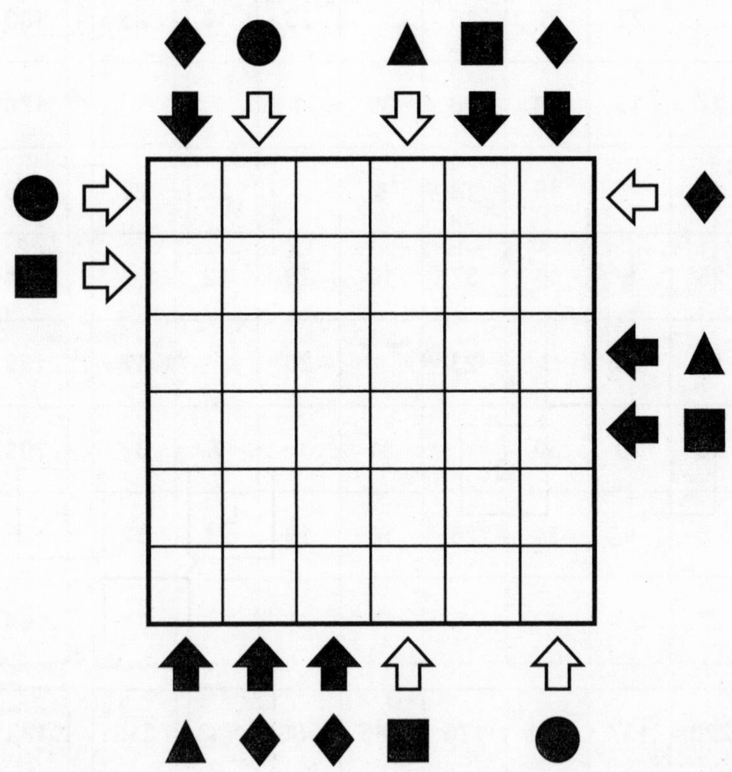

Mind Over Matter

26

Given that the letters are valued 1-26 according to their places in the alphabet, can you crack the mystery code to reveal the missing letter?

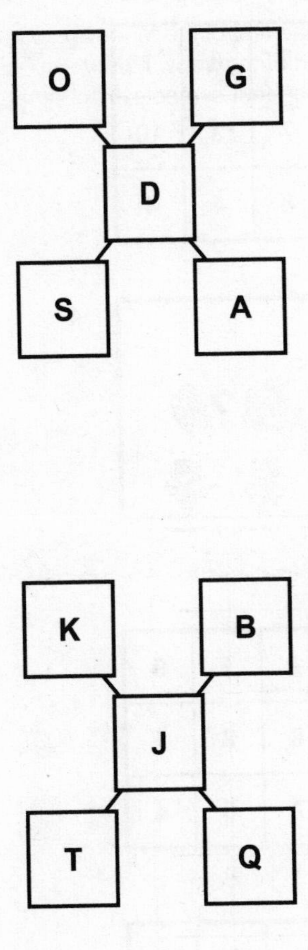

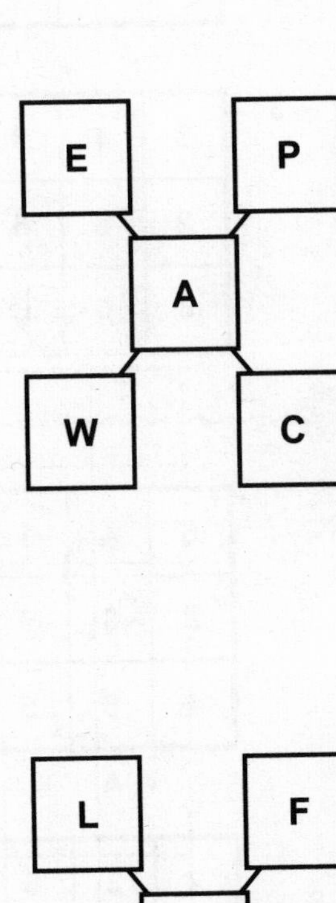

27

Whatever Next?

Which of the four lettered alternatives (A, B, C or D) fits most logically into the empty square?

1

7	9	6
3	2	5
5	4	4

2

2	8	1
7	3	10
6	4	4

3

5	4	3
2	6	6
8	5	6

4

?

6	4	1
8	3	9
1	8	5

A

2	1	9
6	8	1
7	6	4

B

2	3	6
5	8	3
8	2	6

C

4	5	8
8	5	3
2	5	4

D

The Bottom Line

Can you fill each square in the bottom line with the correct digit?

Every square in the solution contains only one digit from each of the lettered lines above, although two or more squares in the solution may contain the same digit.

At the end of every row is a score, which shows:

- **a** the number of digits placed in the correct finishing position on the bottom line, as indicated by a tick; and
- **b** the number of digits which appear on the bottom line, but in a different position, as indicated by a cross.

					SCORE
A	9	5	3	9	✗ ✗
B	2	9	1	9	✓ ✗ ✗
C	4	8	8	2	✓ ✗
D	4	6	2	7	✗
E	6	7	5	8	✗
					✓ ✓ ✓ ✓

29

Combiku

Each horizontal row and vertical column should contain different shapes and different numbers.

Every square will contain one number and one shape and no combination may be repeated anywhere else in the puzzle; so, for instance, if a square contains a 3 and a star, then no other square containing a 3 will also contain a star and no other square with a star will contain a 3.

1 2 3 4 5

			2	
1				
4		3		
				2

Ls in Place

Twelve L-shapes like the ones here need to be inserted in the grid and each L has one hole in it.

There are three pieces of each of the four kinds shown here and any piece may be turned or flipped over before being put in the grid. No pieces of the same kind touch, even at a corner.

The pieces fit together so well that you cannot see any spaces between them; only the holes show. Can you tell where the Ls are?

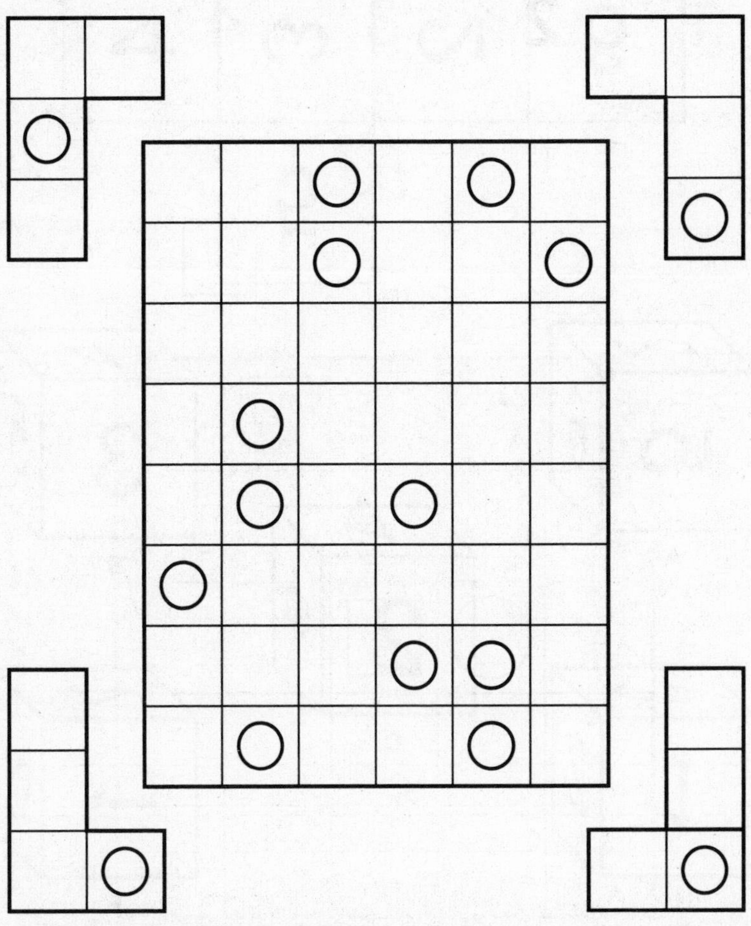

31

Box Clever

When the box below is folded to form a cube, just one of the five options (A, B, C, D or E) can be produced. Which?

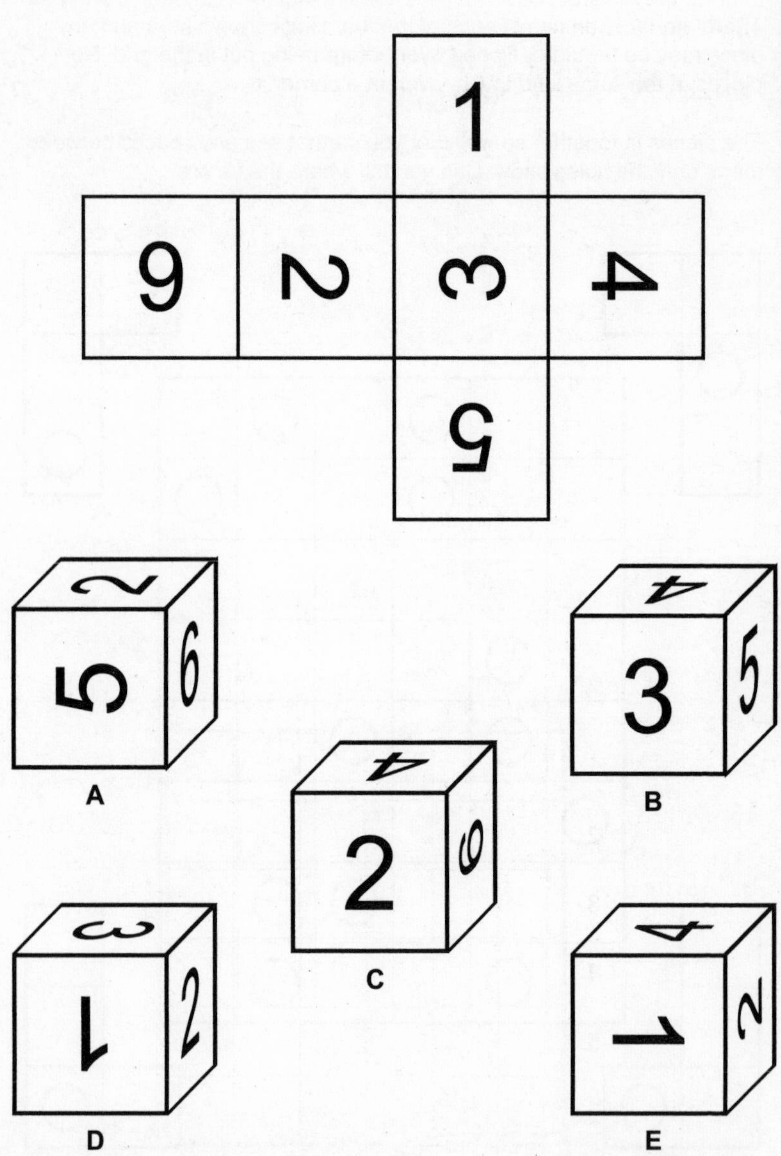

Latin Square

32

The grid should be filled with numbers from 1 to 6, so that each number appears just once in every row and column. The clues refer to the digit totals in the squares, eg A 1 2 3 = 6 means that the numbers in squares A1, A2 and A3 add up to 6.

1 DEF1 = 14

2 EF2 = 9

3 BC3 = 3

4 CD4 = 9

5 CD5 = 4

6 BCD6 = 13

7 A34 = 11

8 B45 = 9

9 C12 = 5

10 D23 = 10

11 E45 = 8

12 AB6 = 9

	A	B	C	D	E	F
1						
2						
3						
4						
5						
6						

33

Number Link

Working from one square to another, horizontally or vertically (never diagonally), draw single continuous paths to pair up each set of two matching numbers. No line may cross another and none may travel through any square containing a number.

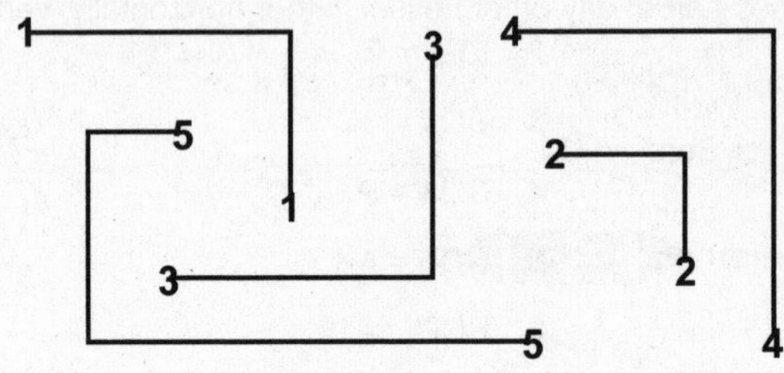

4				4				
3		3				9	2	
6				8	1			
			7					
	8				1			
							2	
		5						
						9	5	
							7	6

Battleships

Can you place the vessels into the diagram? Some parts of vessels or sea squares have already been filled in. A number to the right or below a row or column refers to the number of occupied squares in that row or column.

Any vessel may be positioned horizontally or vertically, but no part of a vessel touches part of any other vessel, either horizontally, vertically or diagonally.

Empty Area of Sea: ≈

Aircraft Carrier:

Battleships:

Cruisers:

Submarines:

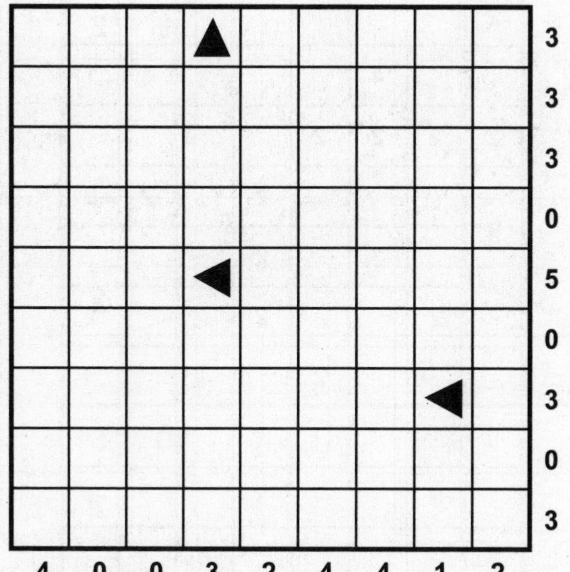

35 Coin Collecting

In this puzzle, an amateur coin collector has been out with his metal detector, searching for booty. He didn't have time to dig up all the coins he found, so has made a grid map, showing their locations, in the hope that if he loses the map, at least no-one else will understand it... However, he didn't count on YOU coming across the strange grid (as seen here). Will you be able to discover the correct number of coins and their precise locations?

Those squares containing numbers are empty, but where a number appears in a square, it indicates how many coins are located in the squares (up to a maximum of eight) surrounding the numbered one, touching it at any corner or side. There is only one coin in any individual square.

Place a circle into every square containing a coin.

			0				
1	1				2	4	3
2							
		4				4	1
2	2	2	2				
				2		2	0
		3		2			
	2			2			2
			2		4		
0							
	3			3			1
1					0		

Slitherlink

Draw a single continuous loop, by connecting the dots. No line may cross the path of another.

The figure inside each set of any four surrounding dots indicates the total number of surrounding lines.

	3	2	2	2	1			2	
2		1		0				0	3
1				2	0	1			
					3	3	2	2	1
3		2	2	1	2				
					3	3	1	1	
2			0						
1				1	1			3	2
	1	2			3	1	1	1	
	1		2	2		1	1		3
	0			2		1	2		
	2	1		2	2	2		2	

37

Spot Numbers

The numbers at the top and on the left side show the quantity of single-digit numbers (1-9) used in that row and column. The numbers at the bottom and on the right show the sum of the digits. A number may appear more than once in a row or column, but no numbers are in squares that touch, even at a corner. One number is already in place.

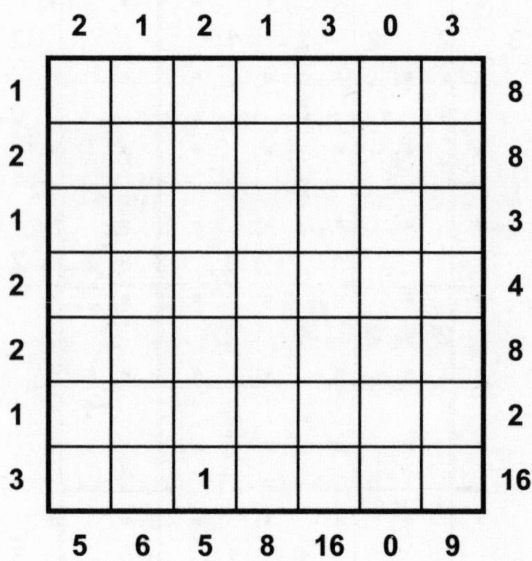

	2	1	2	1	3	0	3	
1								8
2								8
1								3
2								4
2								8
1								2
3			1					16
	5	6	5	8	16	0	9	

Logi-6

Every row and column of this grid should contain one each of the letters A, B, C, D, E and F. In addition, each of the six shapes (marked by thicker lines) should also contain one each of the letters A, B, C, D, E and F. Can you complete the grid?

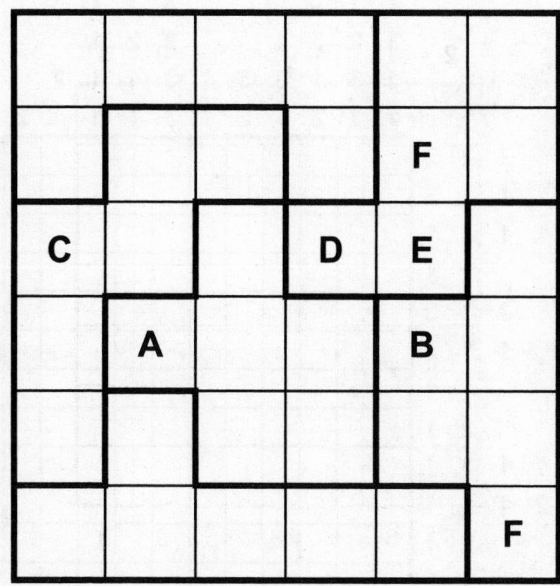

39

Piecework

Place all twelve of the pieces into the grid. Any may be rotated or flipped over, but none may touch another, not even diagonally. The numbers outside the grid refer to the number of consecutive black squares; and each block is separated from the others by at least one white square. For instance, '3 2' could refer to a row with none, one or more white squares, then three black squares, then at least one white square, then two more black squares, followed by any number of white squares.

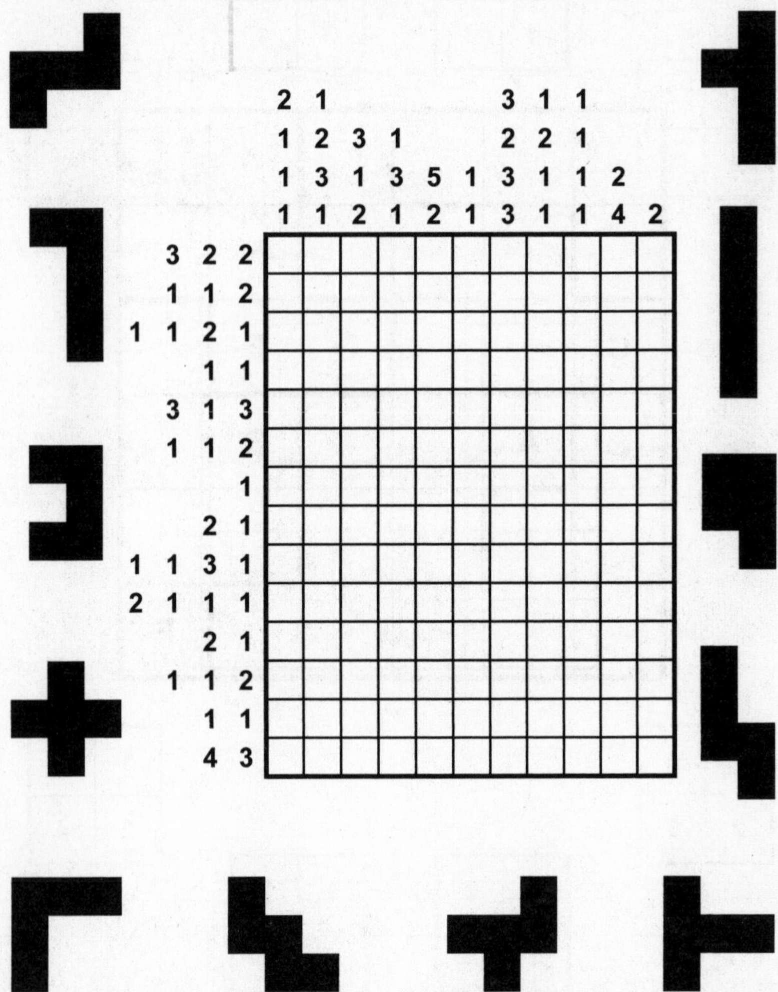

Tile Twister

40

Place the eight tiles into the puzzle grid so that all adjacent numbers on each tile match up. Tiles may be rotated through 360 degrees, but none may be flipped over.

3	2
4	3

2	1
3	4

4	2
2	1

1	4
4	3

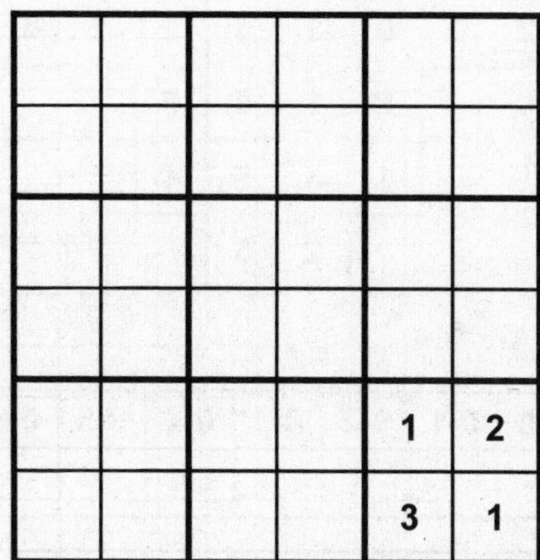

1	3
2	3

1	1
2	4

2	2
1	4

2	3
2	4

41 Domino Placement

A standard set of twenty-eight dominoes has been laid out as shown. Can you draw in the edges of them all? The check-box is provided as an aid, so that you can see which dominoes have been located.

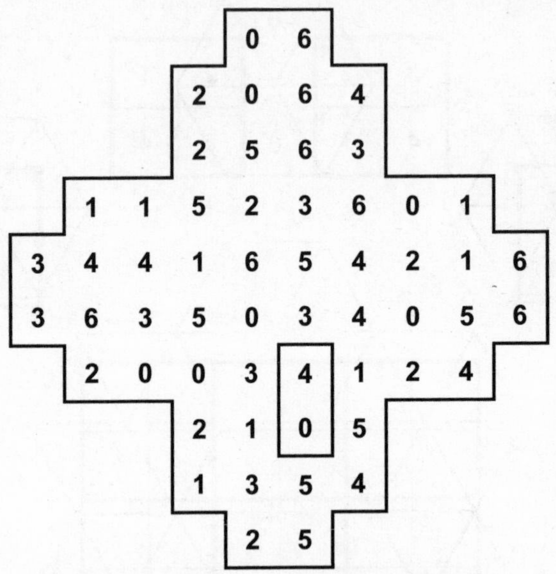

0-0	0-1	0-2	0-3	0-4	0-5	0-6
				✓		

1-1	1-2	1-3	1-4	1-5	1-6	2-2

2-3	2-4	2-5	2-6	3-3	3-4	3-5

3-6	4-4	4-5	4-6	5-5	5-6	6-6

Hexagony

Can you place the hexagons into the grid, so that where any hexagon touches another along a straight line, the contents of both triangles is the same? No rotation of any hexagon is allowed!

43 Simple as A, B, C?

Each of the small squares in the grid below contains either A, B or C. Every row, column and each of the two long diagonals has exactly two of each letter. The information in the clues refers only to the squares in that row or column. To help you solve this problem, we have provided as many clues as we think you will need! Can you tell the letter in each square?

Across

1 Each A is next to and right of a B.
2 The Bs are between the Cs.
5 The Cs are between the As.
6 Each B is next to and right of a C.

Down

1 The As are higher than the Bs.
2 The Cs are between the As.
3 The Bs are between the Cs.
5 The Bs are higher than the As.

	1	2	3	4	5	6
1						
2						
3						
4						
5						
6						

Total Concentration

44

The blank squares below should be filled with whole numbers between 1 and 40 inclusive, any of which may occur more than once, or not at all.

The numbers in every horizontal row add up to the totals on the right, as do the two long diagonal lines; whilst those in every vertical column add up to the totals along the bottom.

Can you discover the missing numbers?

								158
	3	16	13	27		7	34	159
12	8		27	40	18	4		165
14	28	16		12	22	40		176
35		2	19		17	9	13	140
6	3	9		7	15		22	116
	20	10	28		29	30	11	165
21	29		37	3		4	16	148
18		5	31	25	11		38	139
166	120	123	189	141	153	134	182	145

45 Shape Up

Every row and column in this grid originally contained one circle, one diamond, one square, one triangle and two blank squares, although not necessarily in that order.

Every symbol with a black arrow refers to the first of the four symbols encountered when travelling in the direction of the arrow. Every symbol with a white arrow refers to the second of the four symbols encountered in the direction of the arrow.

Can you complete the original grid?

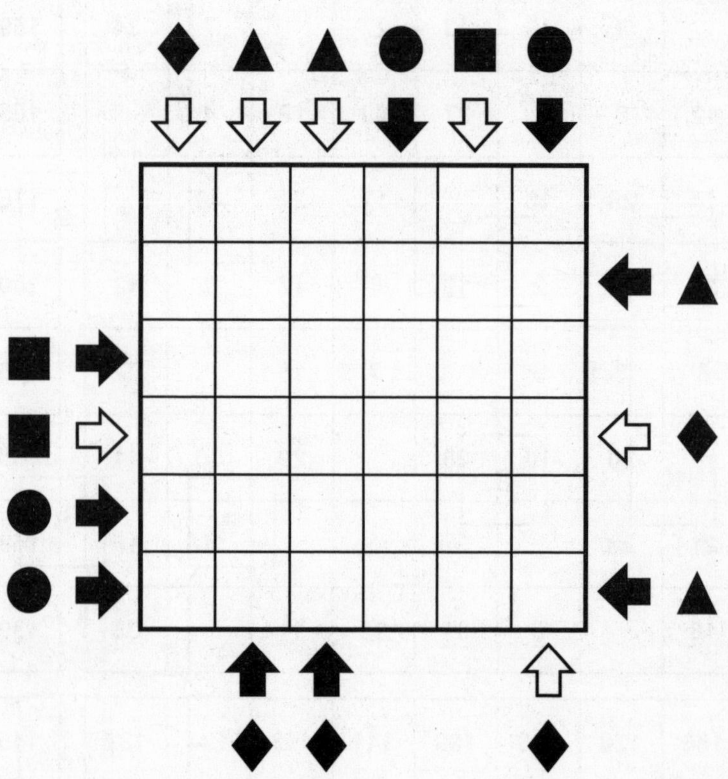

Mind Over Matter

Given that the letters are valued 1-26 according to their places in the alphabet, can you crack the mystery code to reveal the missing letter?

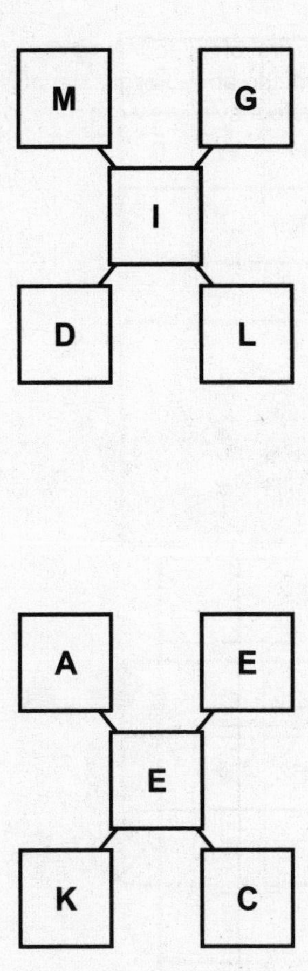

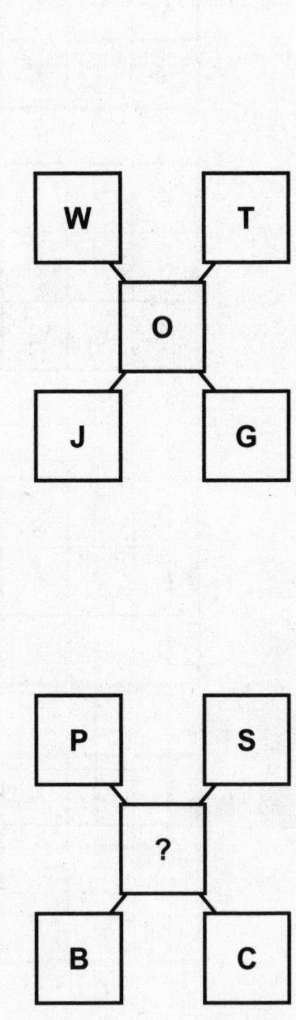

47 Whatever Next?

Which of the four lettered alternatives (A, B, C or D) fits most logically into the empty square?

1

A	N	R
L	V	F
M	I	C

2

B	O	S
M	W	G
N	J	D

3

C	P	T
N	X	H
O	K	E

4

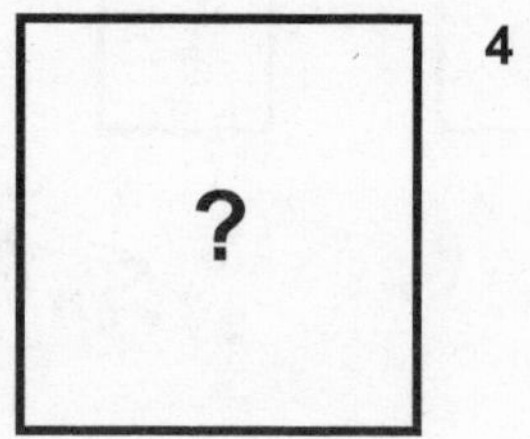

D	Q	U
P	Y	I
Q	J	F

A

D	Q	U
O	Y	I
P	K	F

B

D	Q	U
O	Z	I
P	L	F

C

D	Q	U
O	Y	I
P	L	F

D

The Bottom Line

Can you fill each square in the bottom line with the correct digit?

Every square in the solution contains only one digit from each of the lettered lines above, although two or more squares in the solution may contain the same digit.

At the end of every row is a score, which shows:

a the number of digits placed in the correct finishing position on the bottom line, as indicated by a tick; and

b the number of digits which appear on the bottom line, but in a different position, as indicated by a cross.

					SCORE
A	5	9	8	9	✗ ✗
B	5	1	7	6	✗
C	2	8	6	3	✗
D	2	5	5	8	✓ ✓ ✗
E	3	4	1	3	✗
					✓ ✓ ✓ ✓

49 Combiku

Each horizontal row and vertical column should contain different shapes and different numbers.

Every square will contain one number and one shape and no combination may be repeated anywhere else in the puzzle; so, for instance, if a square contains a 3 and a star, then no other square containing a 3 will also contain a star and no other square with a star will contain a 3.

1 2 3 4 5

	4	3	2	
5				
			4	
4				3
2			3	

Ls in Place

50

Twelve L-shapes like the ones here need to be inserted in the grid and each L has one hole in it.

There are three pieces of each of the four kinds shown here and any piece may be turned or flipped over before being put in the grid. No pieces of the same kind touch, even at a corner.

The pieces fit together so well that you cannot see any spaces between them; only the holes show. Can you tell where the Ls are?

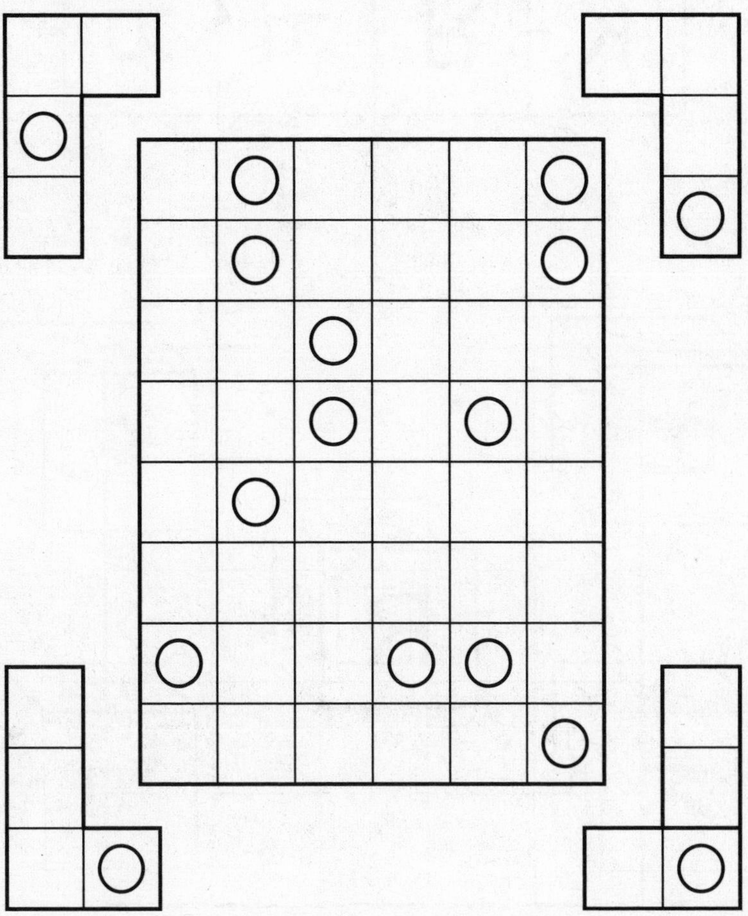

51

Box Clever

When the box below is folded to form a cube, just one of the five options (A, B, C, D or E) can be produced. Which?

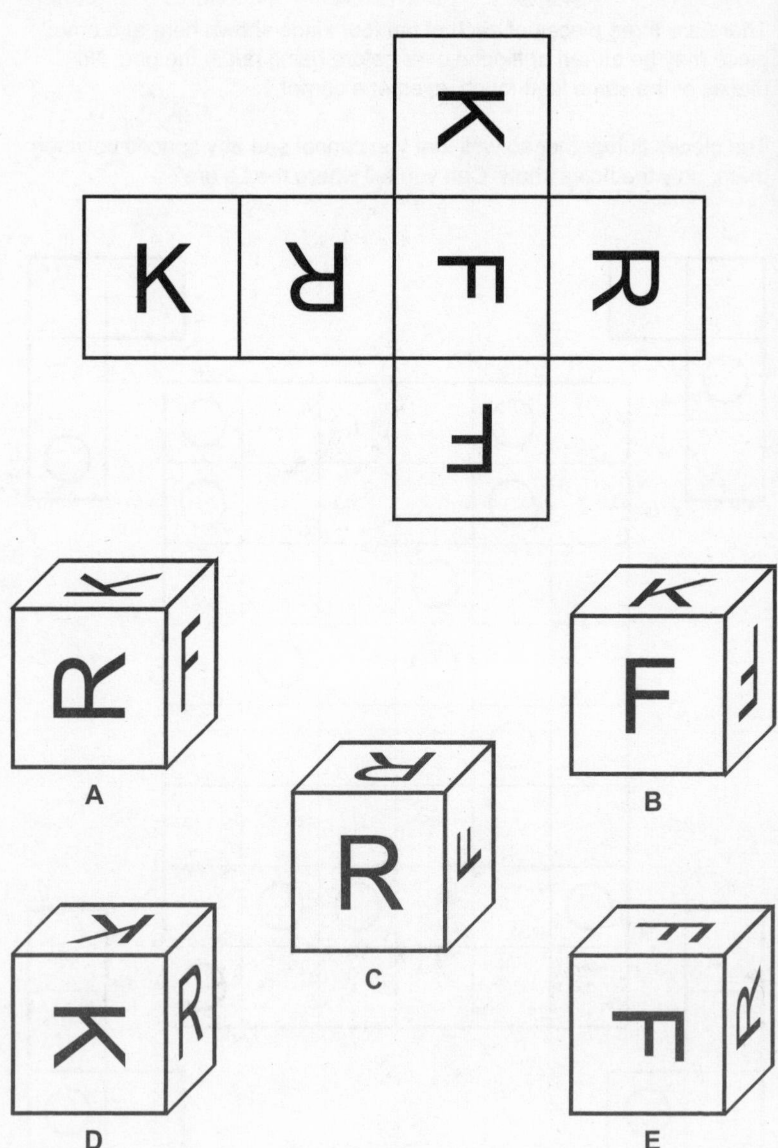

Latin Square

The grid should be filled with numbers from 1 to 6, so that each number appears just once in every row and column. The clues refer to the digit totals in the squares, eg A 1 2 3 = 6 means that the numbers in squares A1, A2 and A3 add up to 6.

1 DEF1 = 14

2 AB2 = 4

3 BCD3 = 9

4 DE4 = 9

5 EF5 = 4

6 BC6 = 4

7 A34 = 7

8 B45 = 11

9 C45 = 6

10 D56 = 7

11 E23 = 10

12 EF4 = 4

	A	B	C	D	E	F
1						
2						
3						
4						
5						
6						

53

Number Link

Working from one square to another, horizontally or vertically (never diagonally), draw single continuous paths to pair up each set of two matching numbers. No line may cross another and none may travel through any square containing a number.

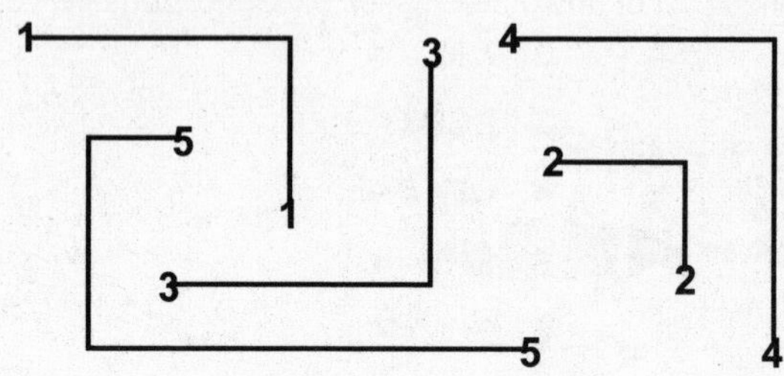

						9	7	1
	4		5			2		
	6					3		
		8						
								1
			4	5	2	3		7
	6							
							9	
8								

Battleships

Can you place the vessels into the diagram? Some parts of vessels or sea squares have already been filled in. A number to the right or below a row or column refers to the number of occupied squares in that row or column.

Any vessel may be positioned horizontally or vertically, but no part of a vessel touches part of any other vessel, either horizontally, vertically or diagonally.

Empty Area of Sea: ≈

Aircraft Carrier:

Battleships:

Cruisers:

Submarines:

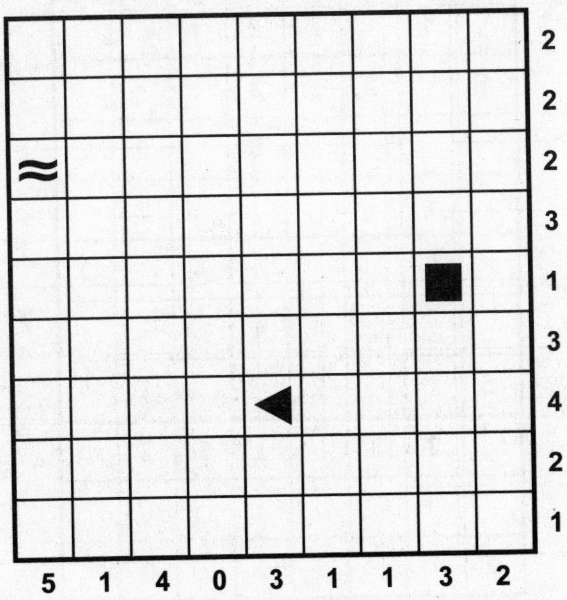

55

Coin Collecting

In this puzzle, an amateur coin collector has been out with his metal detector, searching for booty. He didn't have time to dig up all the coins he found, so has made a grid map, showing their locations, in the hope that if he loses the map, at least no-one else will understand it... However, he didn't count on YOU coming across the strange grid (as seen here). Will you be able to discover the correct number of coins and their precise locations?

Those squares containing numbers are empty, but where a number appears in a square, it indicates how many coins are located in the squares (up to a maximum of eight) surrounding the numbered one, touching it at any corner or side. There is only one coin in any individual square.

Place a circle into every square containing a coin.

		2					
2				2	2	4	3
	1			2	1		
1		2		3			
				5		2	
	1					2	
	3				4		0
			4	4		2	
			2				
	2	0			3	2	
0	1		1			0	

Slitherlink

Draw a single continuous loop, by connecting the dots. No line may cross the path of another.

The figure inside each set of any four surrounding dots indicates the total number of surrounding lines.

1	2	2		3		1			
2				0	3	2	2	1	
					3				
	1		0			3	1		
1		3	1				1	1	2
			0			3	1		
			2	0					
1	2				0		1	2	2
	0			3			1	1	
		0						1	
2		1		1		1	1		
		1		3		3		1	2

57

Spot Numbers

The numbers at the top and on the left side show the quantity of single-digit numbers (1-9) used in that row and column. The numbers at the bottom and on the right show the sum of the digits. A number may appear more than once in a row or column, but no numbers are in squares that touch, even at a corner. One number is already in place.

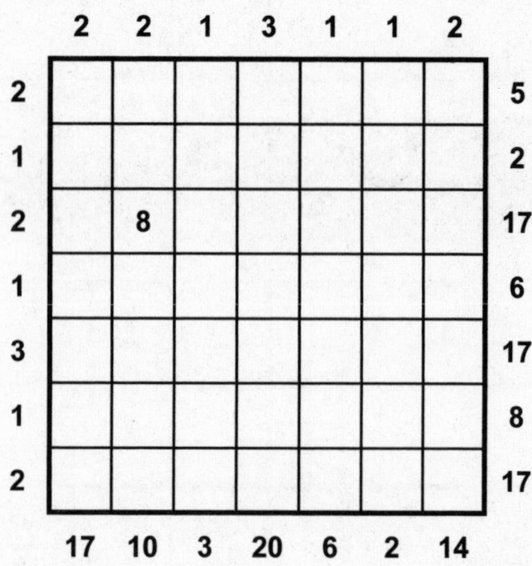

	2	2	1	3	1	1	2	
2								5
1								2
2		8						17
1								6
3								17
1								8
2								17
	17	10	3	20	6	2	14	

Logi-6

58

Every row and column of this grid should contain one each of the letters A, B, C, D, E and F. In addition, each of the six shapes (marked by thicker lines) should also contain one each of the letters A, B, C, D, E and F. Can you complete the grid?

				F	
	D			E	
B				C	
A					E

59 Piecework

Place all twelve of the pieces into the grid. Any may be rotated or flipped over, but none may touch another, not even diagonally. The numbers outside the grid refer to the number of consecutive black squares; and each block is separated from the others by at least one white square. For instance, '3 2' could refer to a row with none, one or more white squares, then three black squares, then at least one white square, then two more black squares, followed by any number of white squares.

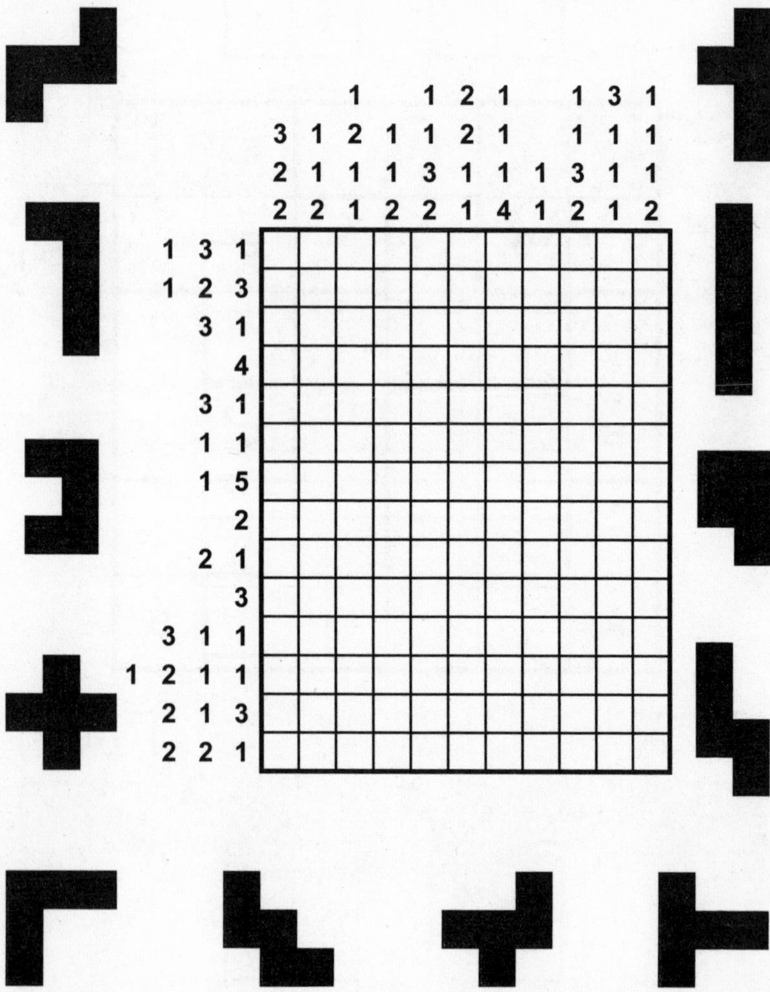

Tile Twister

Place the eight tiles into the puzzle grid so that all adjacent numbers on each tile match up. Tiles may be rotated through 360 degrees, but none may be flipped over.

3	2
4	2

4	4
2	1

2	4
3	4

3	4
3	1

				4	2
				3	3

2	4
4	3

2	1
1	1

2	1
4	3

3	4
1	3

61 Domino Placement

A standard set of twenty-eight dominoes has been laid out as shown. Can you draw in the edges of them all? The check-box is provided as an aid, so that you can see which dominoes have been located.

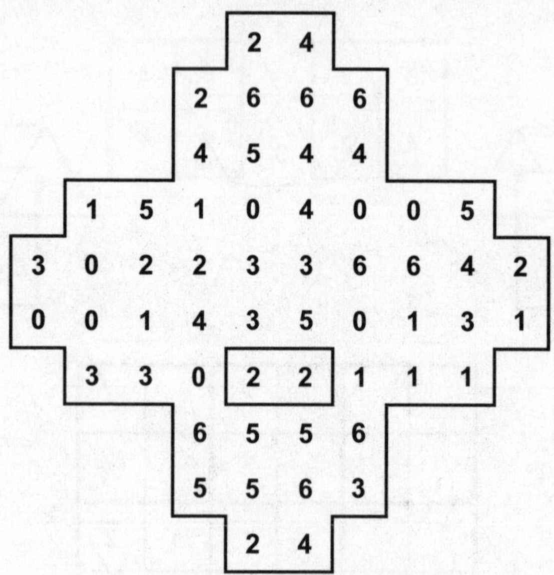

0-0	0-1	0-2	0-3	0-4	0-5	0-6

1-1	1-2	1-3	1-4	1-5	1-6	2-2
						✓

2-3	2-4	2-5	2-6	3-3	3-4	3-5

3-6	4-4	4-5	4-6	5-5	5-6	6-6

Hexagony

Can you place the hexagons into the grid, so that where any hexagon touches another along a straight line, the contents of both triangles is the same? No rotation of any hexagon is allowed!

63 Simple as A, B, C?

Each of the small squares in the grid below contains either A, B or C. Every row, column and each of the two long diagonals has exactly two of each letter. The information in the clues refers only to the squares in that row or column. To help you solve this problem, we have provided as many clues as we think you will need! Can you tell the letter in each square?

Across

1 The Bs are further left than the As.
2 Any three consecutive squares contain three different letters.
3 The Bs are between the As.
5 The As are between the Bs.
6 The As are further right than the Cs.

Down

1 Each B is next to and above a C.
2 The Cs are lower than the Bs.
3 The Cs are between the As.
4 The Cs are between the As.
5 Each A is next to and below a C.
6 The Bs are between the Cs.

	1	2	3	4	5	6
1						
2						
3						
4						
5						
6						

Total Concentration

64

The blank squares below should be filled with whole numbers between 1 and 40 inclusive, any of which may occur more than once, or not at all.

The numbers in every horizontal row add up to the totals on the right, as do the two long diagonal lines; whilst those in every vertical column add up to the totals along the bottom.

Can you discover the missing numbers?

								177
25	5	14	23	22		9		157
19	33	3	16		12	27	13	131
27	7		13	34	16		21	169
		11	30	2	1	15	33	147
14	37	37		26	28		39	212
26	22		17	18		38	10	191
	24	1		32	24	36	35	231
36		32	15		25	6	23	194
214	180	160	166	174	165	170	203	233

65

Shape Up

Every row and column in this grid originally contained one circle, one diamond, one square, one triangle and two blank squares, although not necessarily in that order.

Every symbol with a black arrow refers to the first of the four symbols encountered when travelling in the direction of the arrow. Every symbol with a white arrow refers to the second of the four symbols encountered in the direction of the arrow.

Can you complete the original grid?

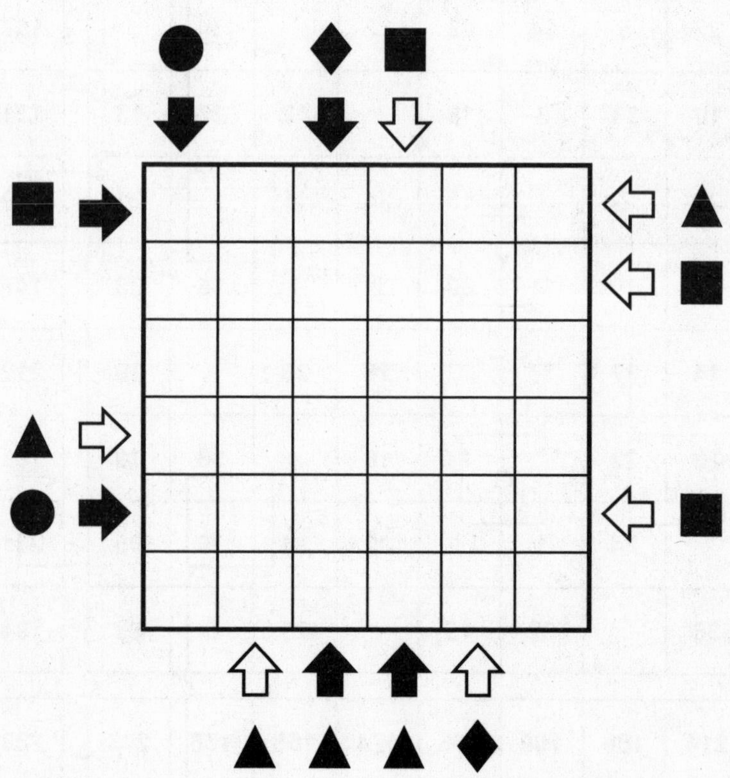

Mind Over Matter

Given that the letters are valued 1-26 according to their places in the alphabet, can you crack the mystery code to reveal the missing letter?

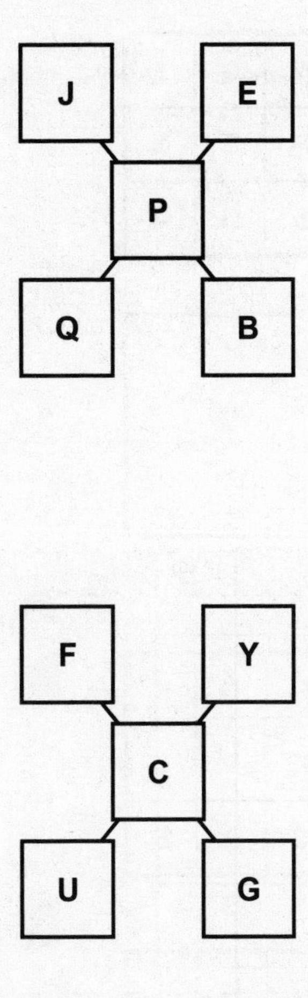

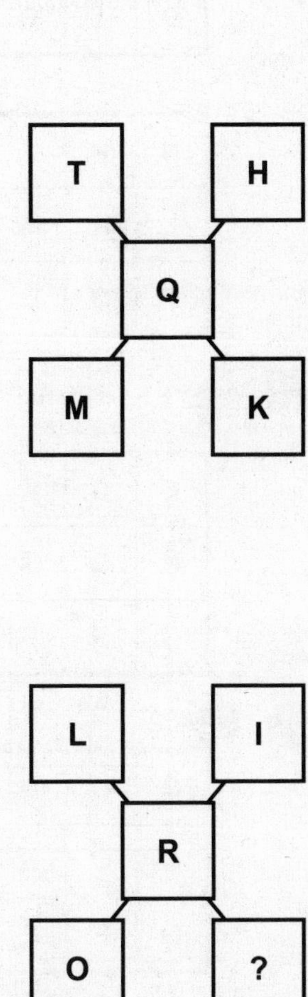

67 Whatever Next?

Which of the four lettered alternatives (A, B, C or D) fits most logically into the empty square?

1

L	R	H
N	T	O
D	I	B

2

M	Q	I
M	S	N
E	H	C

3

N	P	J
L	R	M
F	G	D

4

?

A

O	O	K
K	Q	M
G	H	F

B

P	O	K
K	P	L
G	F	E

C

O	O	K
K	Q	L
G	F	E

D

O	R	I
K	Q	L
F	F	E

The Bottom Line

68

Can you fill each square in the bottom line with the correct digit?

Every square in the solution contains only one digit from each of the lettered lines above, although two or more squares in the solution may contain the same digit.

At the end of every row is a score, which shows:

a the number of digits placed in the correct finishing position on the bottom line, as indicated by a tick; and

b the number of digits which appear on the bottom line, but in a different position, as indicated by a cross.

					SCORE
A	3	8	1	7	✗
B	5	7	6	8	✗
C	2	5	7	1	✗
D	8	1	4	5	✗
E	6	6	2	5	✗ ✗
					✓ ✓ ✓ ✓

Combiku

Each horizontal row and vertical column should contain different shapes and different numbers.

Every square will contain one number and one shape and no combination may be repeated anywhere else in the puzzle; so, for instance, if a square contains a 3 and a star, then no other square containing a 3 will also contain a star and no other square with a star will contain a 3.

1 2 3 4 5

			4	
1		2		
2	4			
3				1

Ls in Place

Twelve L-shapes like the ones here need to be inserted in the grid and each L has one hole in it.

There are three pieces of each of the four kinds shown here and any piece may be turned or flipped over before being put in the grid. No pieces of the same kind touch, even at a corner.

The pieces fit together so well that you cannot see any spaces between them; only the holes show. Can you tell where the Ls are?

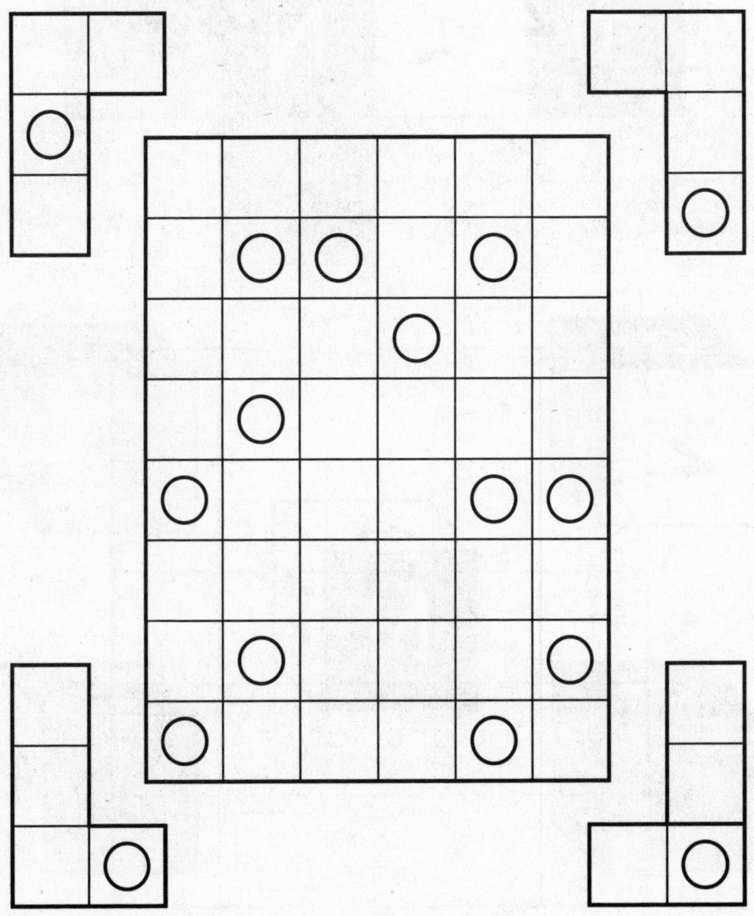

71

Box Clever

When the box below is folded to form a cube, just one of the five options (A, B, C, D or E) can be produced. Which?

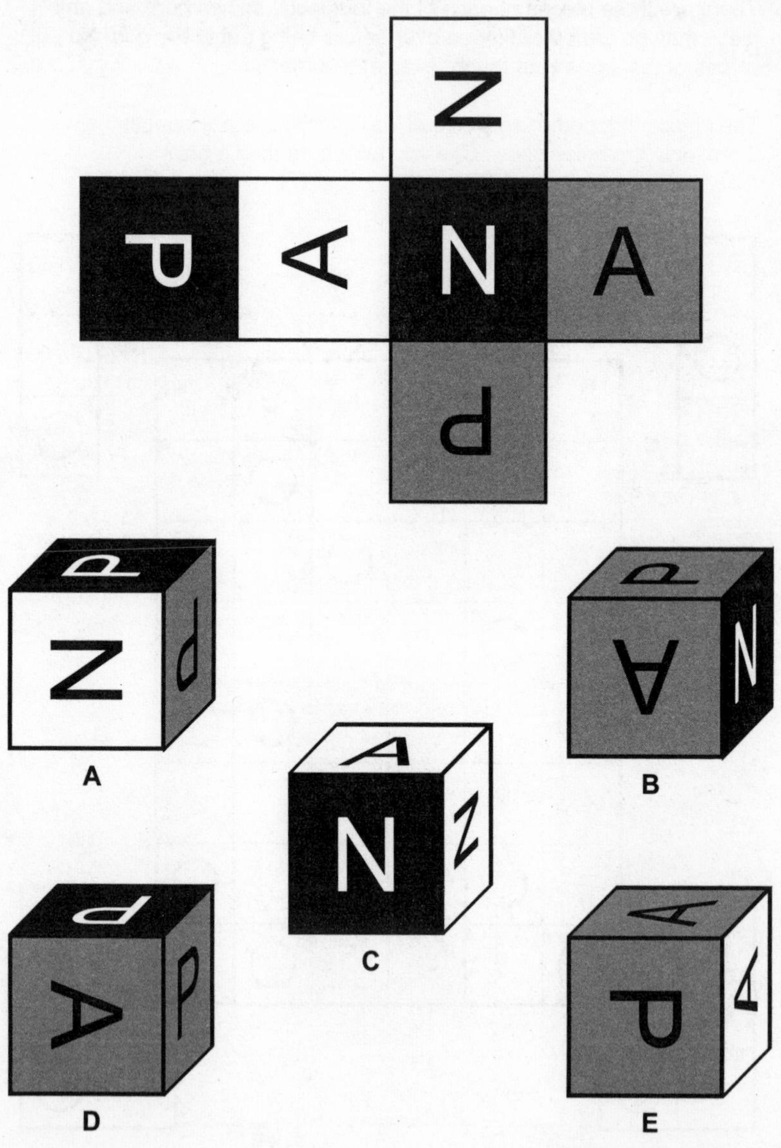

Latin Square

The grid should be filled with numbers from 1 to 6, so that each number appears just once in every row and column. The clues refer to the digit totals in the squares, eg A 1 2 3 = 6 means that the numbers in squares A1, A2 and A3 add up to 6.

1 AB4 = 5

2 AB5 = 8

3 DEF6 = 10

4 A12 = 10

5 B12 = 3

6 C234 = 9

7 D45 = 9

8 E45 = 8

9 F23 = 3

10 CD1 = 8

11 DE2 = 11

12 EF1 = 5

	A	B	C	D	E	F
1						
2						
3						
4						
5						
6						

Number Link

Working from one square to another, horizontally or vertically (never diagonally), draw single continuous paths to pair up each set of two matching numbers. No line may cross another and none may travel through any square containing a number.

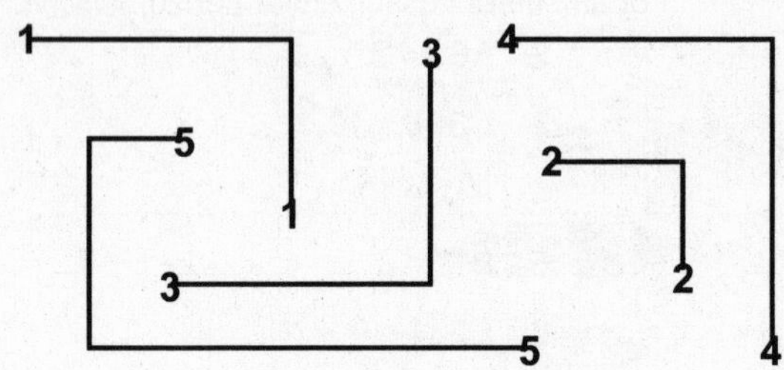

6							6	2
						8	4	
		5					5	2
		7						
							9	
			1				1	
			7					
4	8	9	3					3

Battleships

Can you place the vessels into the diagram? Some parts of vessels or sea squares have already been filled in. A number to the right or below a row or column refers to the number of occupied squares in that row or column.

Any vessel may be positioned horizontally or vertically, but no part of a vessel touches part of any other vessel, either horizontally, vertically or diagonally.

Empty Area of Sea: ≈

Aircraft Carrier:

Battleships:

Cruisers:

Submarines:

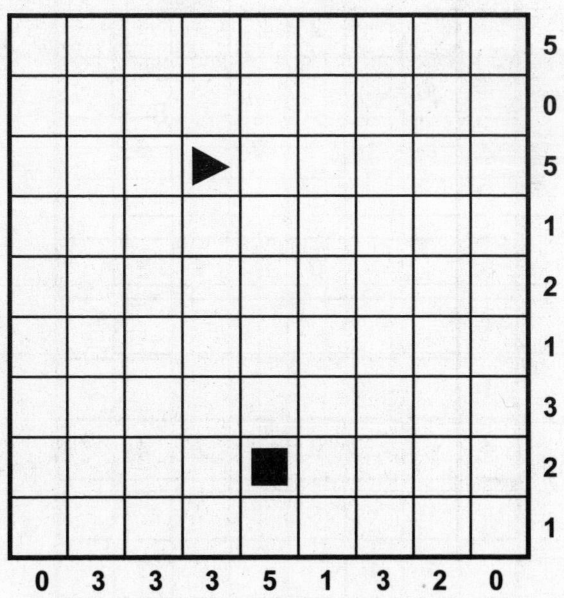

75 Coin Collecting

In this puzzle, an amateur coin collector has been out with his metal detector, searching for booty. He didn't have time to dig up all the coins he found, so has made a grid map, showing their locations, in the hope that if he loses the map, at least no-one else will understand it... However, he didn't count on YOU coming across the strange grid (as seen here). Will you be able to discover the correct number of coins and their precise locations?

Those squares containing numbers are empty, but where a number appears in a square, it indicates how many coins are located in the squares (up to a maximum of eight) surrounding the numbered one, touching it at any corner or side. There is only one coin in any individual square.

Place a circle into every square containing a coin.

2	2	2				2	
		3		1		4	
			2				
	4						
2		1		0		5	
0			0		1	2	
1							
1							2
1			0		2	4	
					3		
	1	1				3	

Slitherlink

Draw a single continuous loop, by connecting the dots. No line may cross the path of another.

The figure inside each set of any four surrounding dots indicates the total number of surrounding lines.

	2	2	1				1		
1		1	1	2	2	0	1		1
1	0		2				1	2	
2				1	1		1		
		3		1	1				
	0						1	0	2
1		0				0			
			3	2		2		1	1
1		0			2		1		3
				0	2	3			
2	1				3		0		
		1	1	1	3				

77

Spot Numbers

The numbers at the top and on the left side show the quantity of single-digit numbers (1-9) used in that row and column. The numbers at the bottom and on the right show the sum of the digits. A number may appear more than once in a row or column, but no numbers are in squares that touch, even at a corner. One number is already in place.

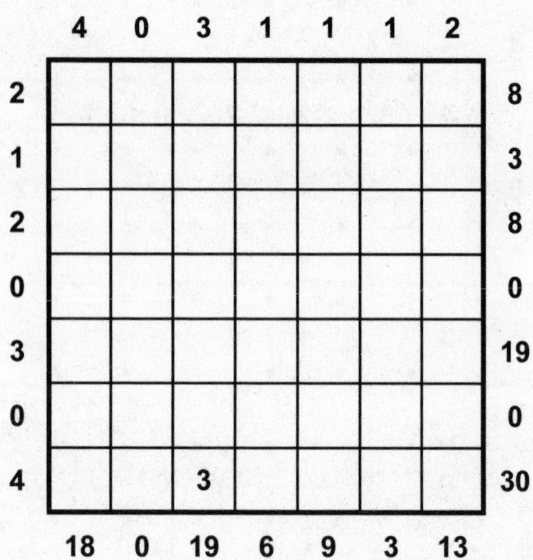

Logi-6

Every row and column of this grid should contain one each of the letters A, B, C, D, E and F. In addition, each of the six shapes (marked by thicker lines) should also contain one each of the letters A, B, C, D, E and F. Can you complete the grid?

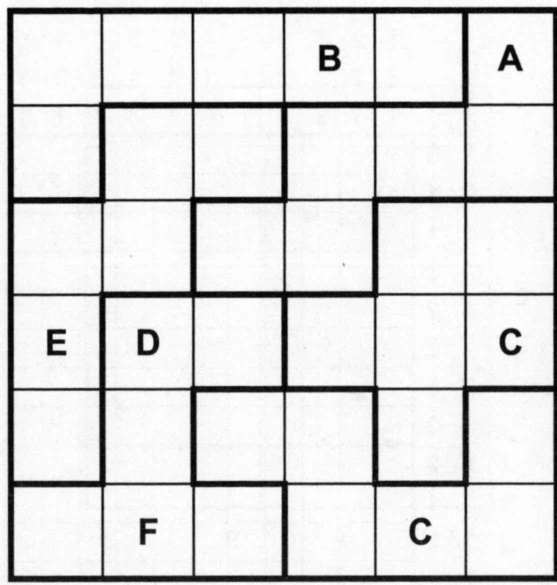

Piecework

Place all twelve of the pieces into the grid. Any may be rotated or flipped over, but none may touch another, not even diagonally. The numbers outside the grid refer to the number of consecutive black squares; and each block is separated from the others by at least one white square. For instance, '3 2' could refer to a row with none, one or more white squares, then three black squares, then at least one white square, then two more black squares, followed by any number of white squares.

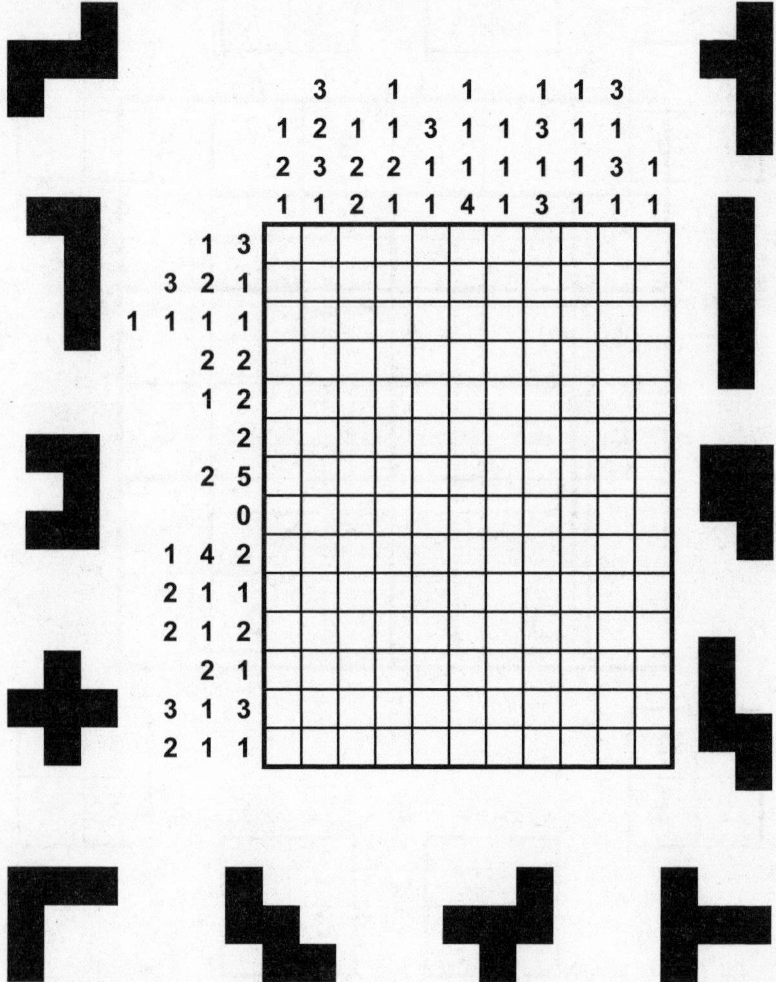

Tile Twister

80

Place the eight tiles into the puzzle grid so that all adjacent numbers on each tile match up. Tiles may be rotated through 360 degrees, but none may be flipped over.

2	2
1	1

4	2
4	1

1	4
1	3

1	1
3	1

2	4				
3	1				

3	3
3	3

3	2
3	1

4	4
3	3

3	1
1	3

81 Domino Placement

A standard set of twenty-eight dominoes has been laid out as shown. Can you draw in the edges of them all? The check-box is provided as an aid, so that you can see which dominoes have been located.

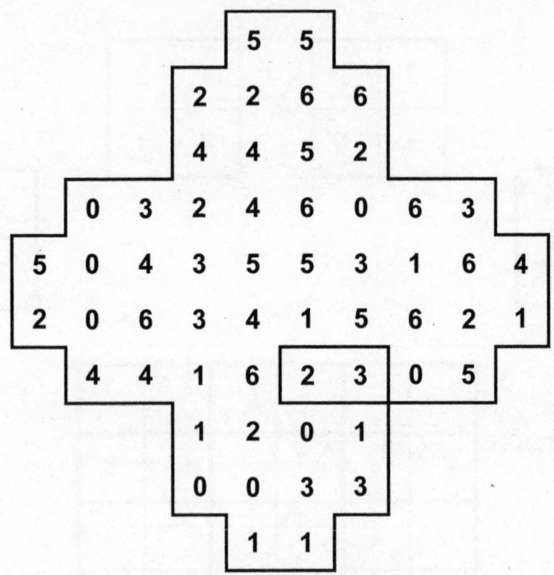

0-0	0-1	0-2	0-3	0-4	0-5	0-6

1-1	1-2	1-3	1-4	1-5	1-6	2-2

2-3	2-4	2-5	2-6	3-3	3-4	3-5
✓						

3-6	4-4	4-5	4-6	5-5	5-6	6-6

Hexagony

Can you place the hexagons into the grid, so that where any hexagon touches another along a straight line, the contents of both triangles is the same? No rotation of any hexagon is allowed!

83 Simple as A, B, C?

Each of the small squares in the grid below contains either A, B or C. Every row, column and each of the two long diagonals has exactly two of each letter. The information in the clues refers only to the squares in that row or column. To help you solve this problem, we have provided as many clues as we think you will need! Can you tell the letter in each square?

Across

1 The Bs are between the Cs.
2 The As are further right than the Cs.
3 The Bs are between the As.
4 The Bs are between the As.
5 The Cs are further right than the As.
6 Any three adjacent squares contain three different letters.

Down

1 The Bs are lower than the As.
2 The Bs are between the Cs.
3 Each C is directly next to and below a B.
4 The As are higher the Bs.
5 The Bs are higher than the Cs.
6 The As are lower than the Cs.

	1	2	3	4	5	6
1						
2						
3						
4						
5						
6						

Total Concentration

84

The blank squares below should be filled with whole numbers between 1 and 40 inclusive, any of which may occur more than once, or not at all.

The numbers in every horizontal row add up to the totals on the right, as do the two long diagonal lines; whilst those in every vertical column add up to the totals along the bottom.

Can you discover the missing numbers?

								143
15	33	2		10		9	2	103
35			20			10	1	139
4	28	28	13	24	32		16	184
25	13		5		37		35	178
4	40	3	23	22	20		9	153
	12	2		8		1		134
1	23	34		30	22	17	9	161
32		31	24	1	21	20	33	183
135	197	125	164	132	181	163	138	182

85 Shape Up

Every row and column in this grid originally contained one circle, one diamond, one square, one triangle and two blank squares, although not necessarily in that order.

Every symbol with a black arrow refers to the first of the four symbols encountered when travelling in the direction of the arrow. Every symbol with a white arrow refers to the second of the four symbols encountered in the direction of the arrow.

Can you complete the original grid?

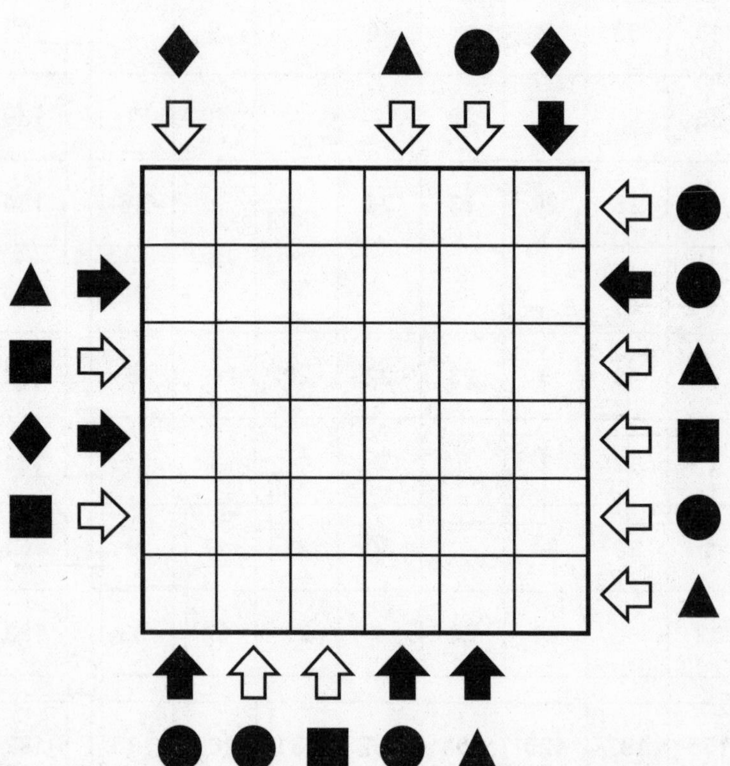

Mind Over Matter

Given that the letters are valued 1-26 according to their places in the alphabet, can you crack the mystery code to reveal the missing letter?

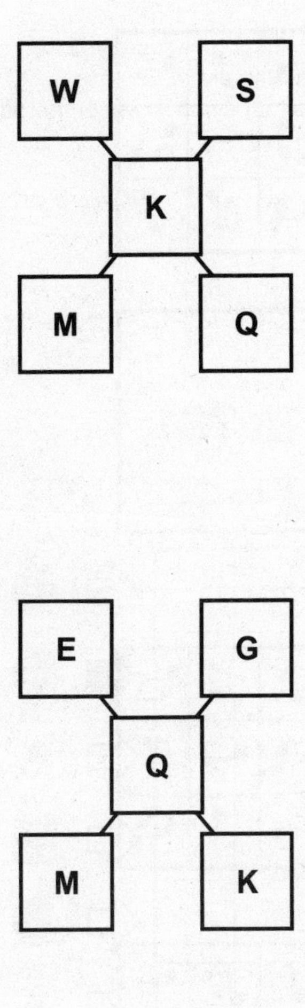

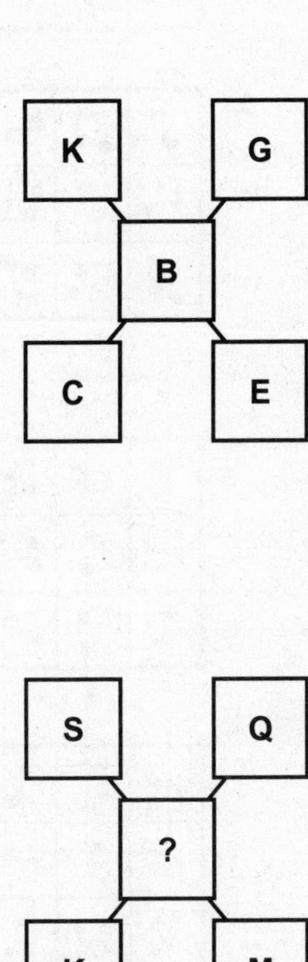

87

Whatever Next?

Which of the four lettered alternatives (A, B, C or D) fits most logically into the empty square?

1

2

3

4

?

A

B

C

D

The Bottom Line

Can you fill each square in the bottom line with the correct digit?

Every square in the solution contains only one digit from each of the lettered lines above, although two or more squares in the solution may contain the same digit.

At the end of every row is a score, which shows:

a the number of digits placed in the correct finishing position on the bottom line, as indicated by a tick; and

b the number of digits which appear on the bottom line, but in a different position, as indicated by a cross.

					SCORE
A	8	3	3	3	✓
B	4	6	5	6	✗ ✗
C	7	4	9	8	✗ ✗ ✗
D	2	3	3	4	✗
E	1	6	9	5	✓ ✗
					✓ ✓ ✓ ✓

89

Combiku

Each horizontal row and vertical column should contain different shapes and different numbers.

Every square will contain one number and one shape and no combination may be repeated anywhere else in the puzzle; so, for instance, if a square contains a 3 and a star, then no other square containing a 3 will also contain a star and no other square with a star will contain a 3.

1 2 3 4 5

		5		
		1		
4			3	
			5	3
	1			

Ls in Place

Twelve L-shapes like the ones here need to be inserted in the grid and each L has one hole in it.

There are three pieces of each of the four kinds shown here and any piece may be turned or flipped over before being put in the grid. No pieces of the same kind touch, even at a corner.

The pieces fit together so well that you cannot see any spaces between them; only the holes show. Can you tell where the Ls are?

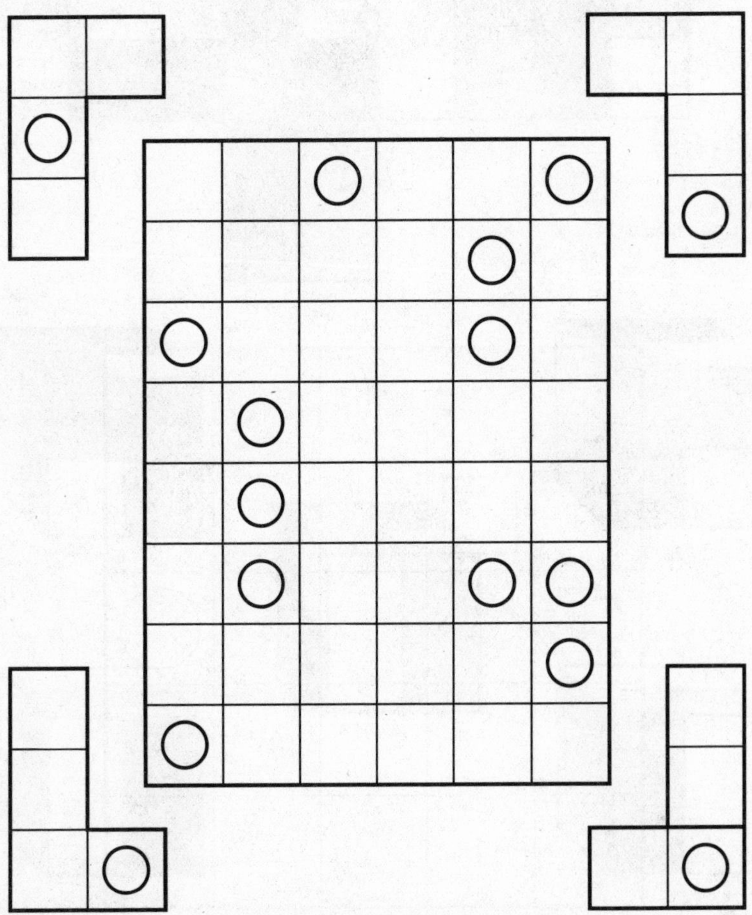

91

Box Clever

When the box below is folded to form a cube, just one of the five options (A, B, C, D or E) can be produced. Which?

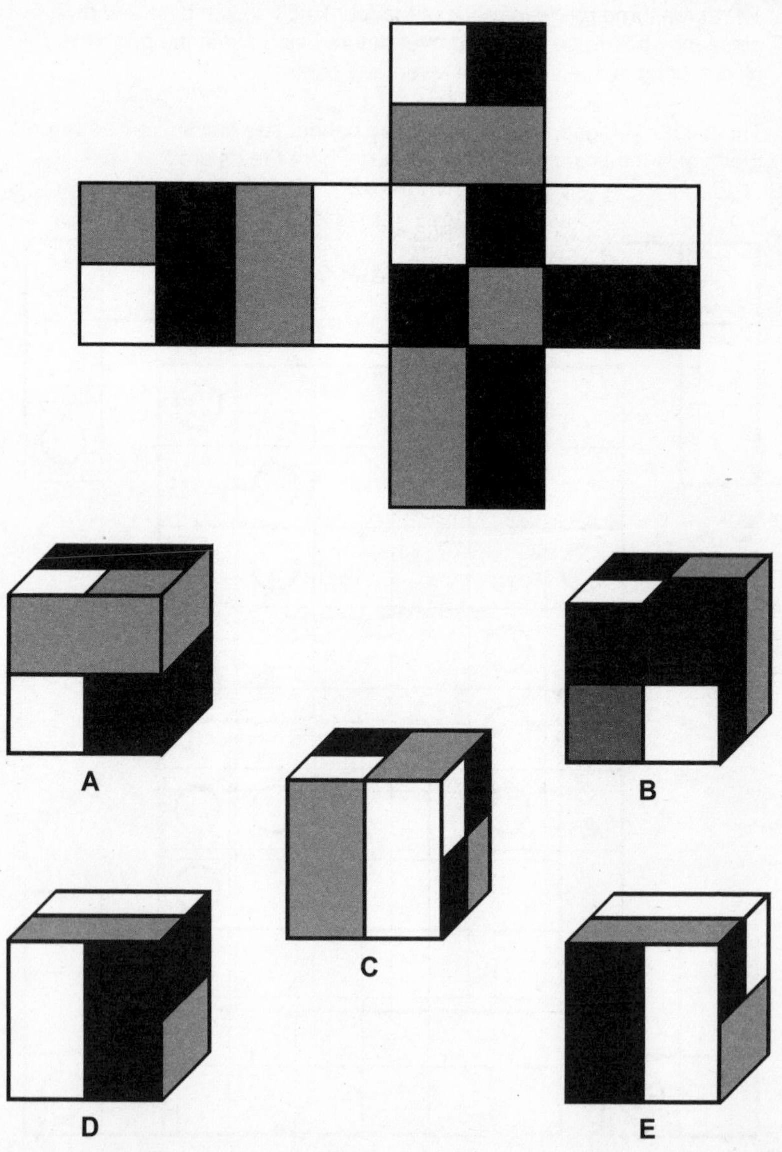

Latin Square

The grid should be filled with numbers from 1 to 6, so that each number appears just once in every row and column. The clues refer to the digit totals in the squares, eg A 1 2 3 = 6 means that the numbers in squares A1, A2 and A3 add up to 6.

1 B12 = 7

2 D12 = 9

3 E123 = 12

4 F56 = 7

5 ABC1 = 13

6 AB2 = 3

7 AB3 = 10

8 DE4 = 3

9 CD5 = 4

10 CD6 = 10

11 A45 = 11

12 B45 = 7

	A	B	C	D	E	F
1						
2						
3						
4						
5						
6						

93

Number Link

Working from one square to another, horizontally or vertically (never diagonally), draw single continuous paths to pair up each set of two matching numbers. No line may cross another and none may travel through any square containing a number.

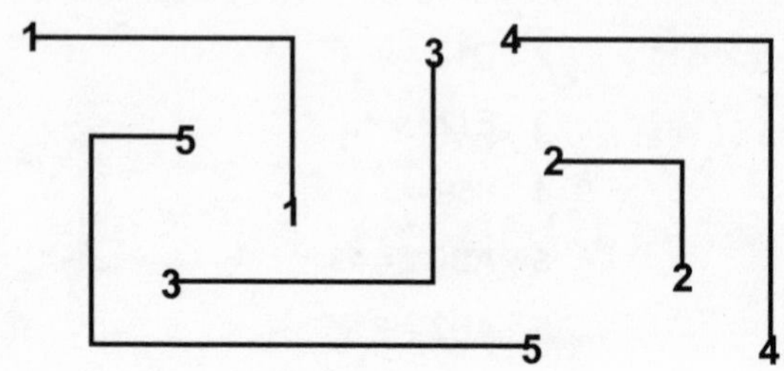

6								
3							3	6
9								
					2	4		
		7	1					
8	5				2	4	8	
7			1	5	9			

Battleships

Can you place the vessels into the diagram? Some parts of vessels or sea squares have already been filled in. A number to the right or below a row or column refers to the number of occupied squares in that row or column.

Any vessel may be positioned horizontally or vertically, but no part of a vessel touches part of any other vessel, either horizontally, vertically or diagonally.

Empty Area of Sea: ≈

Aircraft Carrier:

Battleships:

Cruisers:

Submarines:

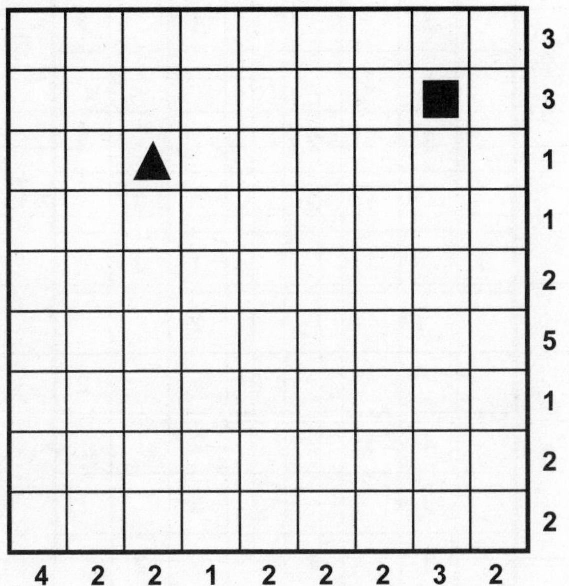

95 Coin Collecting

In this puzzle, an amateur coin collector has been out with his metal detector, searching for booty. He didn't have time to dig up all the coins he found, so has made a grid map, showing their locations, in the hope that if he loses the map, at least no-one else will understand it... However, he didn't count on YOU coming across the strange grid (as seen here). Will you be able to discover the correct number of coins and their precise locations?

Those squares containing numbers are empty, but where a number appears in a square, it indicates how many coins are located in the squares (up to a maximum of eight) surrounding the numbered one, touching it at any corner or side. There is only one coin in any individual square.

Place a circle into every square containing a coin.

					1		
2			1	1			1
	3				1		2
		3		3			
	3		2				2
		1	2			3	
0		1			1	3	
				1	2		
				0			2
	4	3	2		2		
	3				3		
	3		4			2	

Slitherlink

Draw a single continuous loop, by connecting the dots. No line may cross the path of another.

The figure inside each set of any four surrounding dots indicates the total number of surrounding lines.

		2	3		1			0	
1						3	2	1	
	1		1					3	
	3		2		1	0		1	
		3	2	2					
	1						2		2
1	0	1	2			2		1	
1		1	3		2	2		2	2
						1			1
	0		1	3		0		1	
3			1				3	1	1
3	2	3		1	2	2			3

97

Spot Numbers

The numbers at the top and on the left side show the quantity of single-digit numbers (1-9) used in that row and column. The numbers at the bottom and on the right show the sum of the digits. A number may appear more than once in a row or column, but no numbers are in squares that touch, even at a corner. One number is already in place.

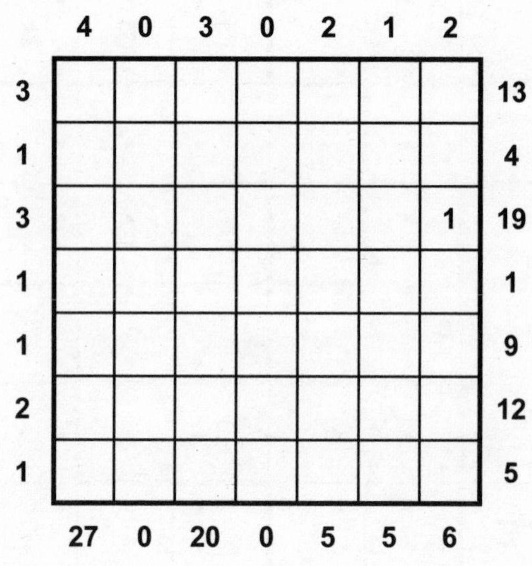

	4	0	3	0	2	1	2	
3								13
1								4
3							1	19
1								1
1								9
2								12
1								5
	27	0	20	0	5	5	6	

Logi-6

Every row and column of this grid should contain one each of the letters A, B, C, D, E and F. In addition, each of the six shapes (marked by thicker lines) should also contain one each of the letters A, B, C, D, E and F. Can you complete the grid?

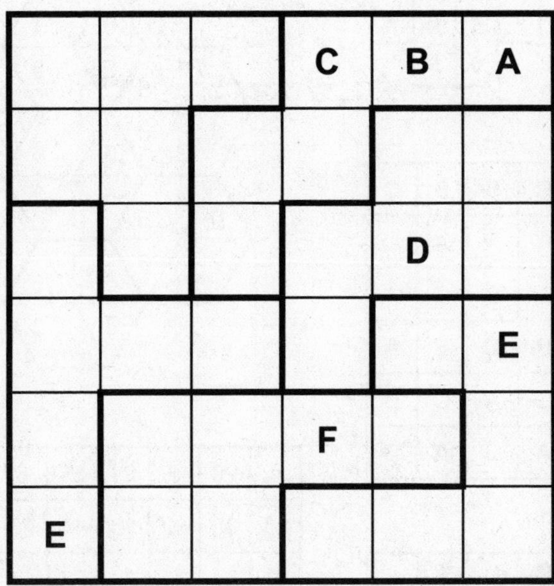

Solutions

1

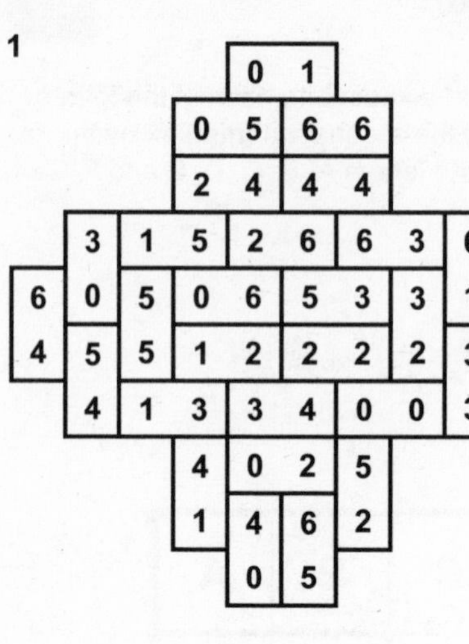

2

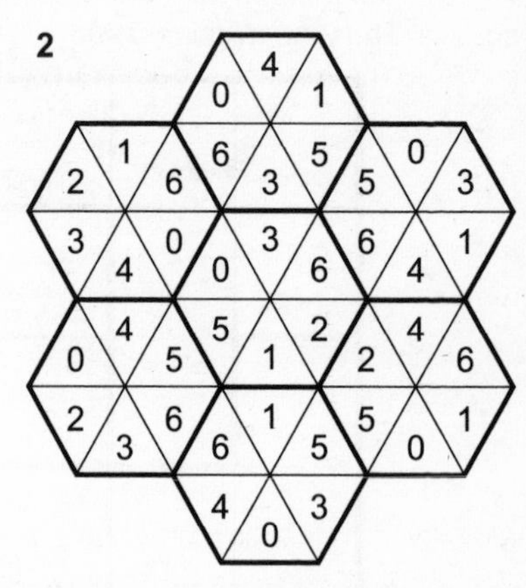

3

A	A	C	B	B	C
C	B	B	A	A	C
B	C	A	B	C	A
A	C	B	C	B	A
B	A	C	A	C	B
C	B	A	C	A	B

4

4	26	5	21	35	6	13	17
18	35	32	16	14	20	32	32
8	34	27	37	25	17	29	21
16	35	33	15	28	24	10	31
38	17	3	20	8	26	19	22
22	18	19	9	28	33	4	30
24	1	40	7	2	13	36	23
9	33	25	25	18	12	39	11

5

◆	■	●		▲	
■	▲	◆		●	
	◆		▲	■	●
●		▲	◆		■
▲	●		■		◆
		■	●	◆	▲

Solutions

6

The value of the letter in the top right square is subtracted from the value of the letter in the top left square, to give the value of the letter in the central square; and the value of the letter in the bottom right square is subtracted from the value of the letter in the bottom left square, to give the value of the letter in the central square. Thus the missing value is 15, so the missing letter is O.

7

B – Each of the smaller squares makes a quarter turn clockwise every time.

8

9754

9

2	4	3	5	1
1	3	5	2	4
5	1	4	3	2
3	2	1	4	5
4	5	2	1	3

Solutions

10

			○		
○				○	
		○			
	○			○	
○			○		○
	○				
	○				○

11
C

12

4	2	6	5	3	1
6	4	1	3	2	5
5	3	4	1	6	2
2	1	3	4	5	6
3	6	5	2	1	4
1	5	2	6	4	3

13

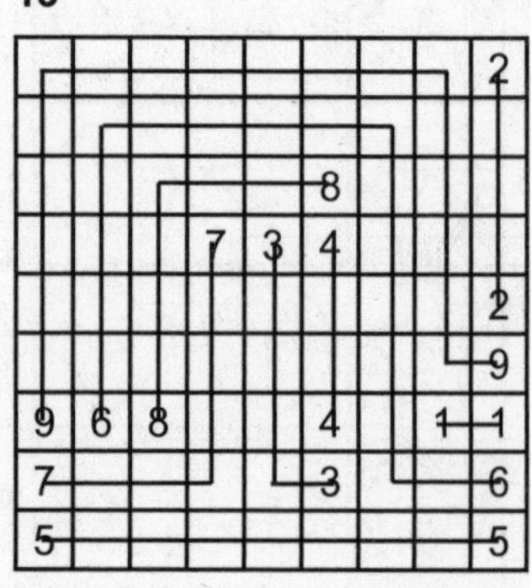

Solutions

14

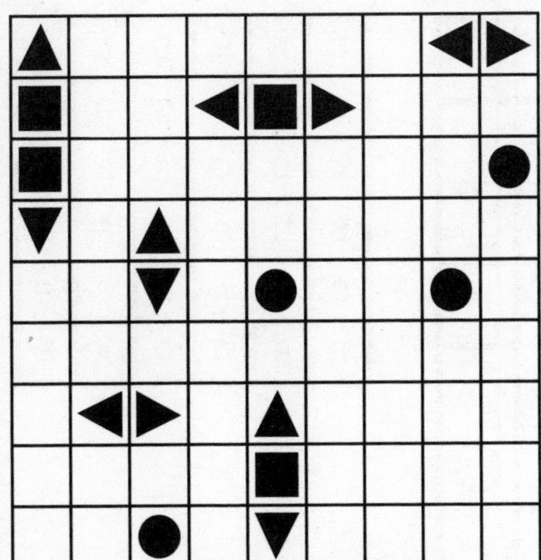

15

0		●	●	3	●		
		3		4	●	3	●
2	●	1		●			1
●			2	●		0	
		0		2			
0				2	●	2	
	0			●		●	
	2		●		3	●	●
●	●		1	1	1	3	●
			2			2	
●	3	●	●	4	●	1	
2	●		●	●			

16

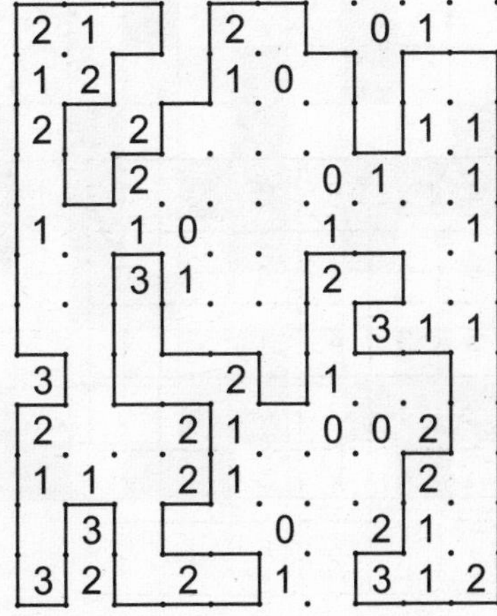

Solutions

17

	1			5		6
	2		8		1	
	2		1			9
9			1			5

18

C	F	B	D	E	A
E	A	F	B	D	C
A	D	C	E	B	F
B	C	E	A	F	D
D	B	A	F	C	E
F	E	D	C	A	B

19

20

4	1	1	4	4	2
4	1	1	3	3	3
4	1	1	3	3	3
2	1	1	4	4	1
2	1	1	4	4	1
3	2	2	1	1	3

Solutions

21

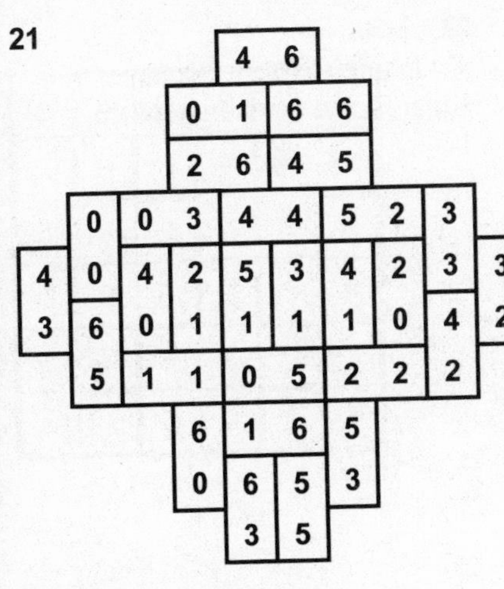

22

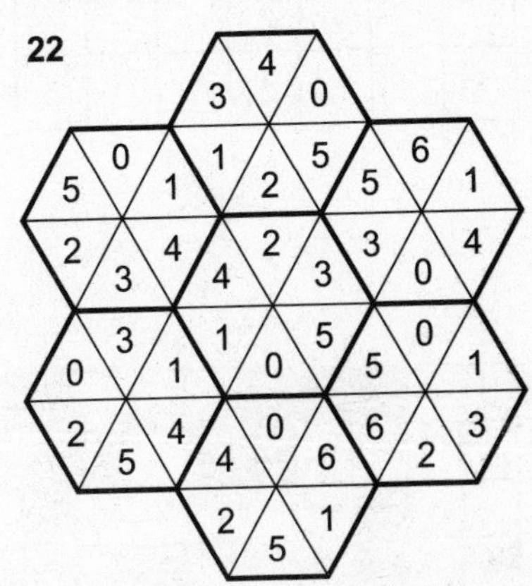

23

B	A	C	A	B	C
A	C	A	B	C	B
A	C	B	A	B	C
C	B	A	C	A	B
C	B	C	B	A	A
B	A	B	C	C	A

24

40	21	5	15	35	23	16	25
27	15	14	20	39	1	24	36
16	22	19	18	8	36	22	29
25	6	38	37	10	28	12	18
19	24	3	23	13	20	19	17
26	20	30	33	31	17	7	37
40	9	34	26	18	19	21	32
27	20	38	4	11	21	22	21

25

	▲	●	◆	■	
	●	■	▲		◆
◆	■			●	▲
●	◆	▲	■		
■		◆		▲	●
▲			●	◆	■

Solutions

26

The value of the letter in the bottom right square is subtracted from the value of the letter in the bottom left square, and this sum is subtracted from the sum total of the values of the letters in the two top squares, to give the value of the letter in the central square. Thus the missing value is 14, so the missing letter is N.

27

A – In each vertical column of three squares, the numbers total 15.

28

8992

29

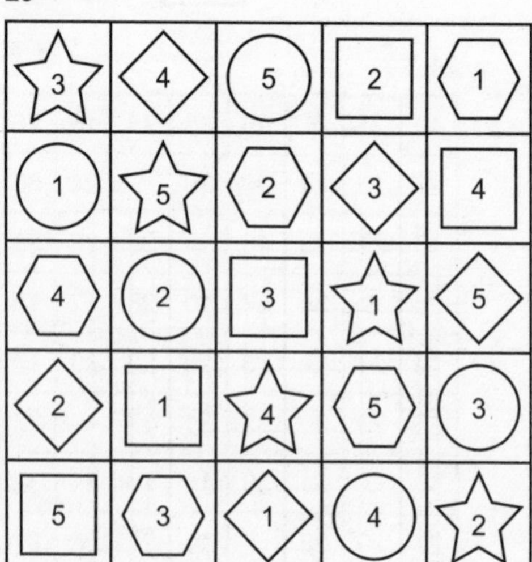

Solutions

30

31

D

32

1	2	4	5	3	6
2	3	1	6	4	5
6	1	2	4	5	3
5	4	6	3	2	1
4	5	3	1	6	2
3	6	5	2	1	4

33

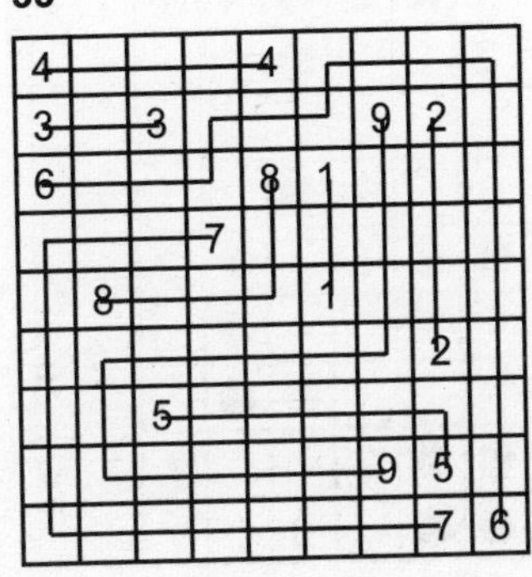

Solutions

34

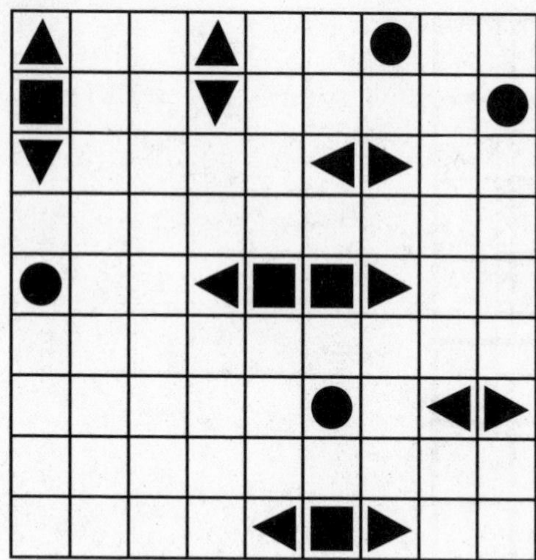

35

			0			●	●
1	1				2	4	3
2	●		●		●		●
	●	4	●	●	●	4	1
2	2	2	2		●		
●				2		2	0
	●	3		2	●		
	2	●	●	2		●	2
			2		4	●	
0					●	●	
	3	●	●	3			1
1	●	●	●		0		

36

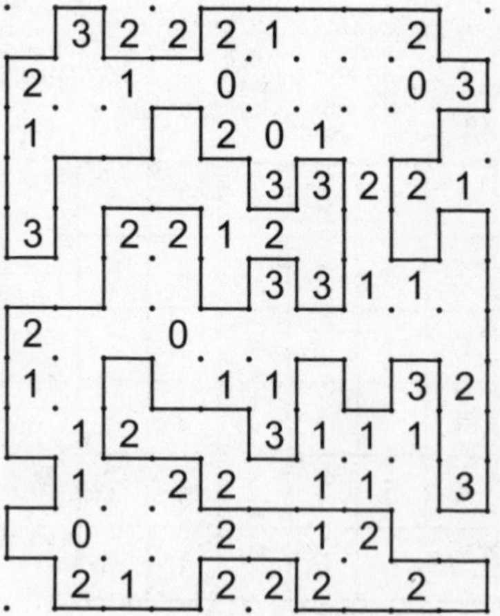

Solutions

37

			8			
	6					2
				3		
3						1
		4		4		
2						
		1		9		6

38

D	E	C	F	A	B
B	D	E	A	F	C
C	B	F	D	E	A
F	A	D	C	B	E
A	F	B	E	C	D
E	C	A	B	D	F

39

40

2	1	1	1	1	4
4	2	2	4	4	3
4	2	2	4	4	3
3	2	2	1	1	2
3	2	2	1	1	2
4	3	3	3	3	1

Solutions

41

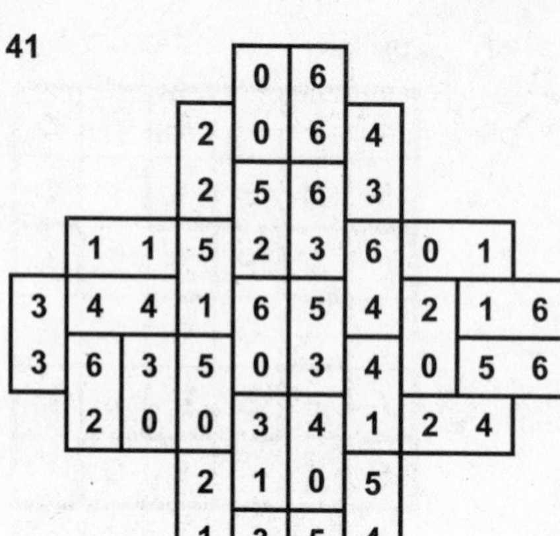

42

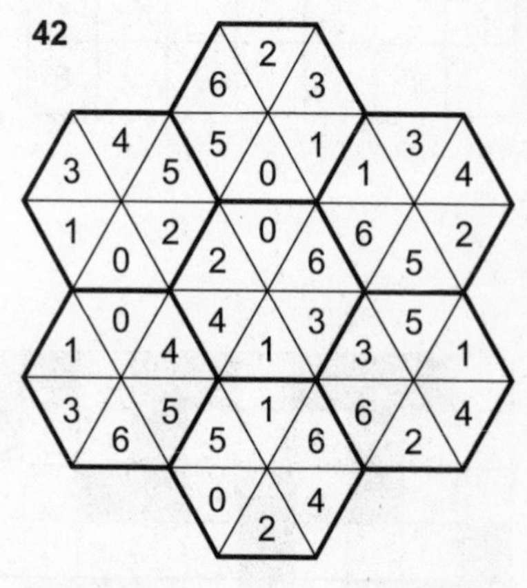

43

C	B	A	C	B	A
A	A	C	B	B	C
A	C	B	C	A	B
B	C	B	A	A	C
B	A	C	B	C	A
C	B	A	A	C	B

44

24	3	16	13	27	35	7	34
12	8	33	27	40	18	4	23
14	28	16	19	12	22	40	25
35	19	2	19	26	17	9	13
6	3	9	15	7	15	39	22
36	20	10	28	1	29	30	11
21	29	32	37	3	6	4	16
18	10	5	31	25	11	1	38

45

▲	■			◆	●
◆		●		■	▲
■		▲	●		◆
	▲	■	◆	●	
	●	◆	▲		■
●	◆		■	▲	

Solutions

46

The value of the letter in the central square is the average of the values of the letters in the other four squares. Thus the missing value is 10, so the missing letter is J.

47

D – The letters move forwards one place in the alphabet each time.

48

8554

49

1	4	3	2	5
5	3	2	1	4
3	1	5	4	2
4	2	1	5	3
2	5	4	3	1

Solutions

50

51

D

52

2	4	1	3	5	6
1	3	5	4	6	2
3	2	6	1	4	5
4	5	2	6	3	1
5	6	4	2	1	3
6	1	3	5	2	4

53

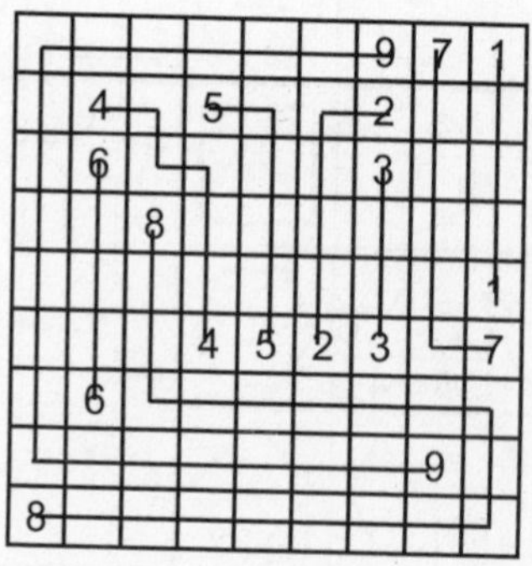

Solutions

54

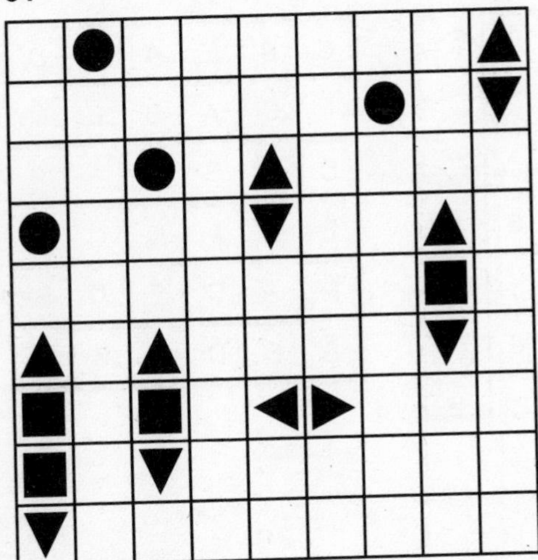

55

	●	2			●		●
2			●	2	2	4	3
●	1			2	1	●	●
1		2	●	3			
			●	5	●	2	
	1			●	●	2	
	3	●	●	●	4		0
●	●		4	4	●	2	
●			2	●		●	
●	2	0		●	3	2	●
0	1	●	1			0	

56

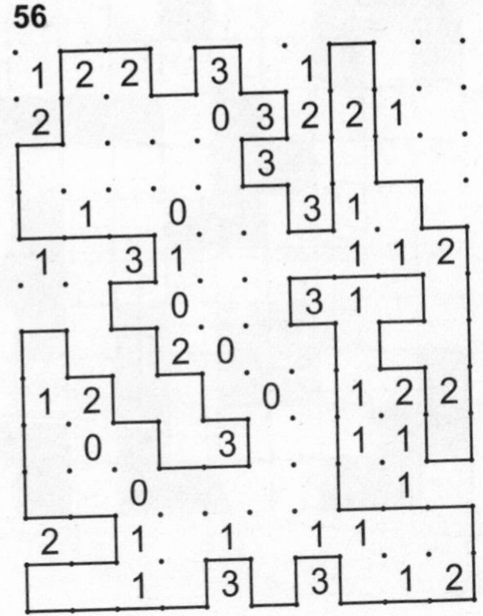

Solutions

57

	2		3			
					2	
	8		9			
						6
8		3		6		
						8
9			8			

58

C	B	E	A	F	D
F	D	A	B	E	C
D	C	B	E	A	F
B	E	F	D	C	A
E	A	C	F	D	B
A	F	D	C	B	E

59

60

1	1	1	3	3	2
1	2	2	4	4	2
1	2	2	4	4	2
4	4	4	3	3	3
4	4	4	3	3	3
2	3	3	1	1	4

Solutions

61

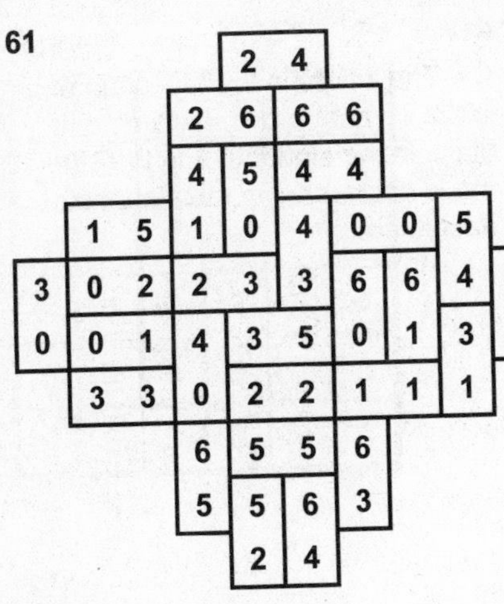

62

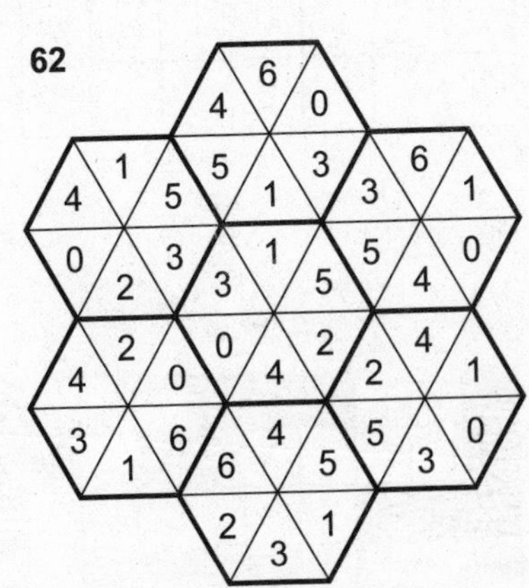

63

B	B	A	A	C	C
C	A	B	C	A	B
A	B	C	B	C	A
A	C	B	C	A	B
B	A	C	A	B	C
C	C	A	B	B	A

64

25	5	14	23	22	30	9	29
19	33	3	16	8	12	27	13
27	7	31	13	34	16	20	21
28	27	11	30	2	1	15	33
14	37	37	12	26	28	19	39
26	22	31	17	18	29	38	10
39	24	1	40	32	24	36	35
36	25	32	15	32	25	6	23

65

	■		◆	▲	●
●		◆	■		▲
▲	◆	■		●	
■	▲		●	◆	
		●	▲	■	◆
◆	●	▲			■

66

The value of the letters in the bottom two squares are multiplied together, then subtracted from the values of the letters in the top two squares multiplied together, to give the value of the letter in the central square. Thus the missing value is 6, so the missing letter is F.

67

C – The letters in the four squares in the corners move forwards one place in the alphabet and the others move backwards in the alphabet each time.

68

4236

69

5	2	1	4	3
4	1	5	3	2
1	3	2	5	4
2	4	3	1	5
3	5	4	2	1

Solutions

70

71

B

72

6	2	5	3	1	4
4	1	3	6	5	2
5	6	4	2	3	1
1	4	2	5	6	3
3	5	1	4	2	6
2	3	6	1	4	5

73

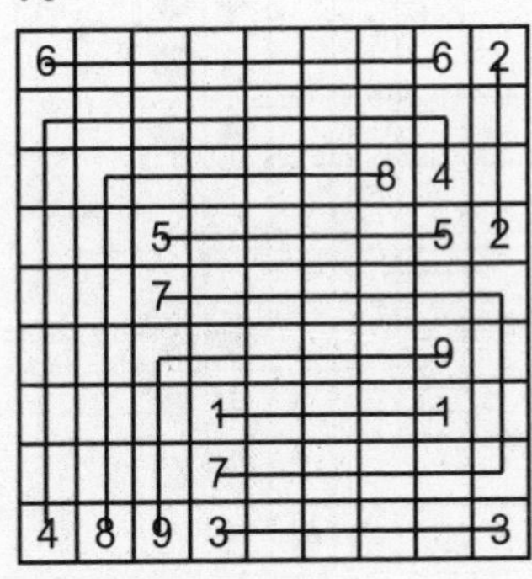

Solutions

74

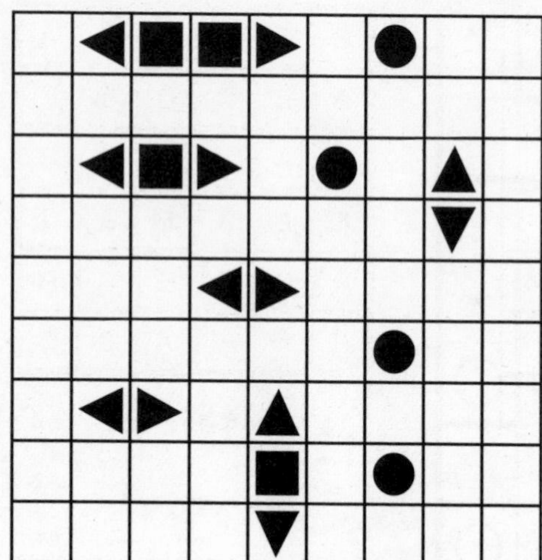

75

2	2	2				2	●
●	●	3	●	1		4	●
●		●	2			●	●
●	4					●	●
2	●	1		0		5	●
						●	●
0			0		1	2	
1							
1	●					●	2
1			0		2	4	●
					3	●	●
●	1	1	●	●	●	3	

76

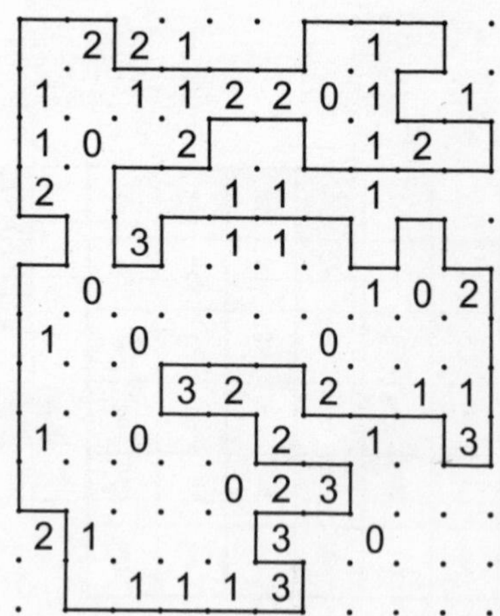

Solutions

77

1		7				
					3	
2			6			
6		9				4
9		3		9		9

78

C	E	D	B	F	A
A	B	C	D	E	F
F	A	B	C	D	E
E	D	A	F	B	C
D	C	F	E	A	B
B	F	E	A	C	D

79

80

1	4	4	3	3	3
2	4	4	3	3	3
2	4	4	3	3	3
3	1	1	1	1	2
3	1	1	1	1	2
1	3	3	1	1	2

Solutions

81

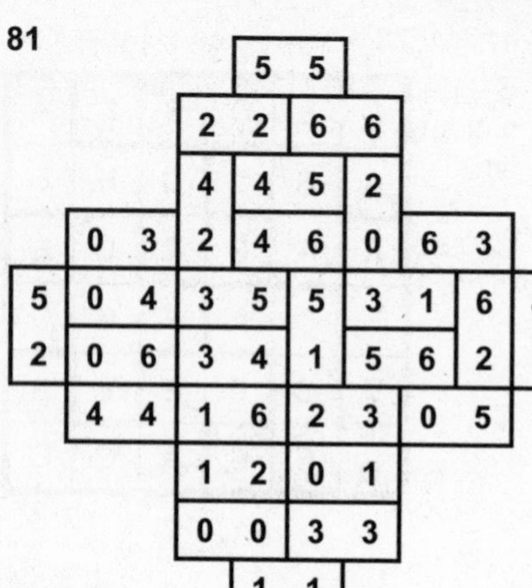

82

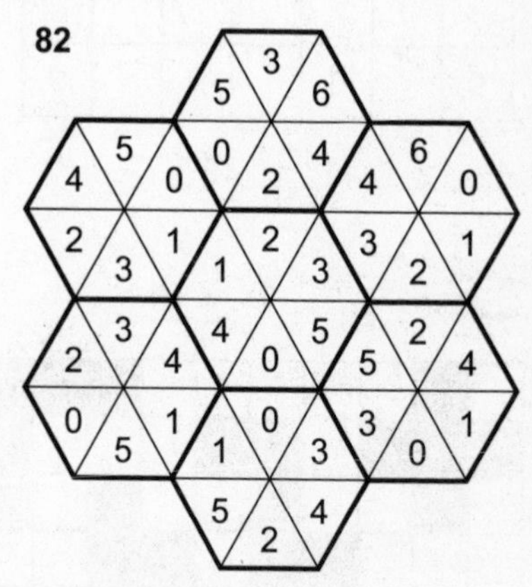

83

A	C	B	A	B	C
C	B	C	A	A	B
C	A	B	B	A	C
A	B	C	C	B	A
B	A	A	C	C	B
B	C	A	B	C	A

84

15	33	2	30	10	2	9	2
35	27	16	20	18	12	10	1
4	28	28	13	24	32	39	16
25	13	9	5	19	37	35	35
4	40	3	23	22	20	32	9
19	12	2	24	8	35	1	33
1	23	34	25	30	22	17	9
32	21	31	24	1	21	20	33

85

■	▲	●			◆
		▲	◆	■	●
	◆	■	▲	●	
◆	●		■		▲
▲	■		●	◆	
●		◆		▲	■

Solutions

86

In each group, move from the top left square, to the top right, bottom right, bottom left, then central square. The values of the letters are all prime numbers which either ascend or descend consecutively in value. Thus the missing value is 7, so the missing letter is G.

87

B – Each set of nine squares makes a quarter turn anticlockwise every time.

88

8945

89

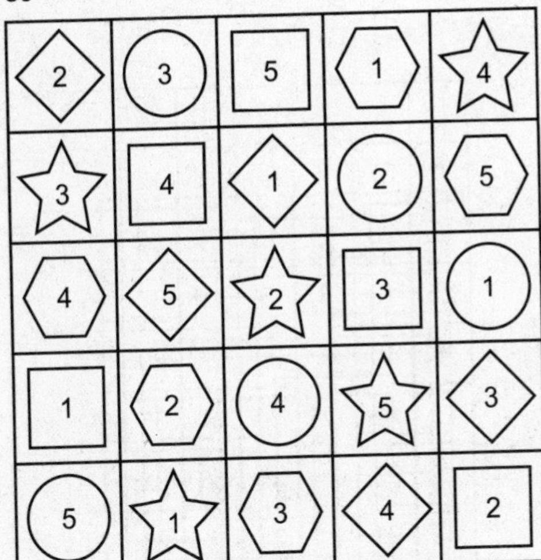

Solutions

90

91

C

92

2	5	6	4	3	1
1	2	3	5	4	6
4	6	2	1	5	3
6	3	5	2	1	4
5	4	1	3	6	2
3	1	4	6	2	5

93

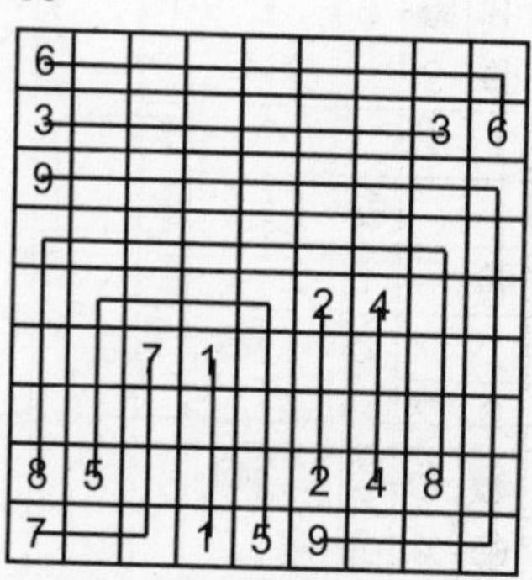

Solutions

94

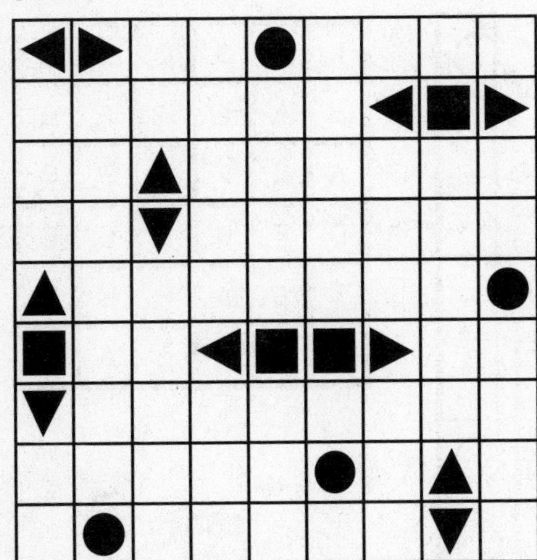

95

					1		
2	●		1	1		●	1
●	3		●		1		2
●		3	●	3			●
●	3	●	2		●		2
		1	2			3	●
0		1		●	1	3	●
		●		1	2		●
●	●			0		●	2
	4	3	2		2		
●	3	●	●		3	●	
	3	●	4	●	●	2	

96

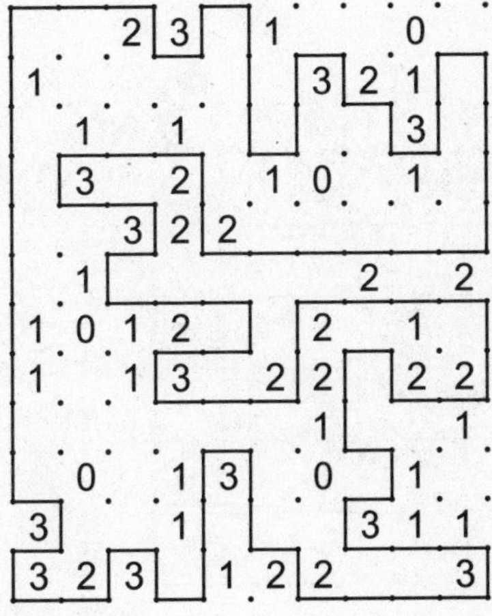

Solutions

97

4		4				5
				4		
9		9				1
				1		
9						
		7			5	
5						

98

F	E	D	C	B	A
B	A	E	D	F	C
A	C	F	E	D	B
D	F	B	A	C	E
C	B	A	F	E	D
E	D	C	B	A	F